REVISE AQA GCSE
Science A

REVISION GUIDE
Foundation

Series Consultant: Harry Smith

Authors: Sue Kearsey, Nigel Saunders and Peter Ellis

THE REVISE AQA SERIES
Available in print or online

Online editions for all titles in the Revise AQA series are available Spring 2013.

Presented on our ActiveLearn platform, you can view the full book and customise it by adding notes, comments and weblinks.

Print editions

Science A Revision Guide Foundation	9781447942108
Science A Revision Workbook Foundation	9781447942184

Online editions

Science A Revision Guide Foundation	9781447942214
Science A Revision Workbook Foundation	9781447942184

Print and online editions are also available for Science (Higher), Additional Science (Foundation and Higher) and Extension Units.

This Revision Guide is designed to complement your classroom and home learning, and to help prepare you for the exam. It does not include all the content and skills needed for the complete course. It is designed to work in combination with Pearson's main AQA GCSE Science 2011 Series.

To find out more visit:
www.pearsonschools.co.uk/aqagcsesciencerevision

ALWAYS LEARNING

PEARSON

Contents

- -

A small bit of small print

AQA publishes Sample Assessment Material and the Specification on its website. This is the official content and this book should be used in conjunction with it. The questions in Now try this have been written to help you practise every topic in the book. Remember: the real exam questions may not look like this.

Target grades

Target grade ranges are quoted in this book for some of the questions. Students targeting this grade range should be aiming to get most of the marks available. Students targeting a higher grade should be aiming to get all of the marks available.

1-to-1 page match with the Core Foundation Workbook ISBN 978-1-447-942184

A healthy diet

A healthy diet contains the right amounts and proportions of NUTRIENTS and energy that the body needs to stay healthy.

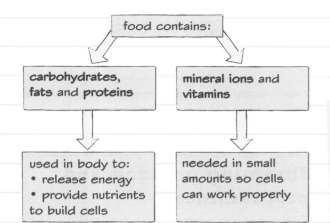

food contains:

carbohydrates, fats and proteins	mineral ions and vitamins

used in body to: • release energy • provide nutrients to build cells	needed in small amounts so cells can work properly

A person who does not eat a balanced diet may become MALNOURISHED.

So what we eat can affect our health.

Possible effects include:
- being very overweight or underweight
- **deficiency diseases** caused by too little of a nutrient
- conditions such as **Type 2 diabetes**.

Anything with this Spec Skills sticker is helping you to *apply* your knowledge.

Worked example D-C

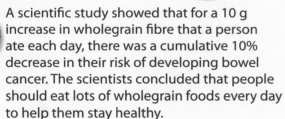

A scientific study showed that for a 10 g increase in wholegrain fibre that a person ate each day, there was a cumulative 10% decrease in their risk of developing bowel cancer. The scientists concluded that people should eat lots of wholegrain foods every day to help them stay healthy.

Do the results of this study support this conclusion? Give a reason for your answer.

(2 marks)

The results do support this conclusion, because the more fibre the person eats the lower their risk of getting bowel cancer.

You will not be expected to know the effect of fibre in the diet, but you will be expected to answer questions like this about the effect of food on health. You will be given data to work with.

Now try this

1 Name two types of nutrients in our diet that give us energy. *(2 marks)*

2 What is meant by the term malnourished? *(1 mark)*

Controlling mass

Metabolic rate

METABOLIC RATE is the rate at which all the chemical reactions are carried out in the body.

Metabolic rate is affected by many factors:

- how much muscle you have
- how much exercise you do
- some INHERITED FACTORS (factors in your genes).

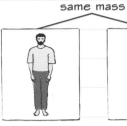

same mass

bigger muscles so less fat

smaller muscles so more fat

A man usually has a higher metabolic rate than a woman of the same mass, because muscle cells use lots more energy than other cells, including fat cells.

The body gains energy by eating food. Energy is EXPENDED (used) during exercise. The balance between energy taken in and energy expended affects your mass.

more energy expended in exercise than gained in food

more energy gained in food than expended in exercise

body loses mass   body gains mass

Remember: the correct scientific word for your 'weight' is mass.

Slimming products and programmes

Slimming programmes and slimming food products claim to help you lose mass. Slimming programmes include guidance about what to eat and how to exercise, as well as providing support to help you keep to targets.

You may be asked to interpret data on claims for slimming products or programmes in your exam.

Worked example   target D-C

SPEC AQA SKILL

The chart shows the average loss of mass in people on three different slimming programmes compared with a group who only exercised.

The makers of Programme B claim theirs is the best slimming programme. Does the graph support this claim? Give reasons for your answer. *(2 marks)*

Weight loss after 12 weeks, and then after one year, was greater on the other two programmes. So it is not the best of these programmes for losing weight.

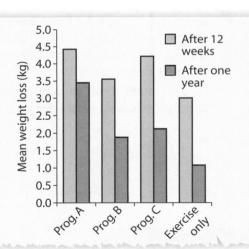

Now try this

target G-E

1 What does metabolic rate mean? *(1 mark)*

target D-C

2 In the chart above, which slimming programme was the best for losing weight? Give two reasons for your answer. *(3 marks)*

3 Explain why eating less and exercising more can help you lose mass. *(3 marks)*

Lifestyle and disease

LIFESTYLE is the way we live, including what we eat and what we do, which affects how active we are. Lifestyle factors can harm health and lead to disease.

Exercise and disease

A person who exercises regularly is more likely to stay healthy than a person who doesn't.

benefits of exercise → better weight control ⇒ better health

Inherited factors

INHERITED FACTORS (genes) are not lifestyle factors, but they can affect health. For example, some people have genes that give them a higher blood cholesterol level than other people who eat the same diet.

When we study the effect of lifestyle factors on disease, we must compare people with similar inherited factors so that we get results that can be trusted.

Worked example

In a study, 522 overweight people of similar age who were at risk of developing diabetes were separated into two groups. One group was given advice on how to live more healthily, the other received no advice (control group). After 4 years 11% of the advised group and 23% of the control group had developed diabetes.

The scientists concluded that living healthily reduces the risk of developing diabetes. Do the data support the scientists' conclusion? Give reasons for your answer. *(3 marks)*

If you were asked to evaluate data like this you need to comment on how reliable the results are. Reliability increases with larger numbers, and is also increased by having a control group to make it a fair test.

The data do support the conclusion because 11% of the advised group developed diabetes. This is much less than the 23% of the control group. We can trust the study because it contained a large group (522) of people, of similar age, who all started with the same problems.

EXAM ALERT!

The second mark in this answer is given for explaining why the results can be trusted.

Students have struggled with questions like this in recent exams – **be prepared!**

Now try this

 target G-E

1 What causes a deficiency disease? *(1 mark)*

 target D-C

2 Drinking sugary drinks every day can lead to health problems. Why? *(1 mark)*

3 Explain why exercise can increase a person's chances of staying healthy. *(2 marks)*

Pathogens and infection

Microorganisms that cause disease are called PATHOGENS. Pathogens include some bacteria and viruses. When a few pathogens INFECT us (get inside our bodies) they can reproduce very rapidly. Large numbers of pathogens can make us ill.

Bacteria are much smaller than our cells.

bacterium

Bacteria may release TOXINS (poisons) that make us feel ill. Some types of bacteria invade and destroy body cells.

Viruses are much smaller than bacteria.

virus

Viruses take over a body cell's DNA causing the cell to make TOXINS or causing damage when new viruses are made.

Semmelweis

Ignaz Semmelweis was a doctor in the mid-1800s who wondered why many women died of infection soon after childbirth.

People didn't know about microorganisms then, so they didn't know what caused infection.

| Semmelweis realised that doctors might transfer infection between patients on their hands. | → | He insisted that doctors wash their hands before examining each patient. | → | Death rates fell rapidly in wards where doctors washed their hands. |

Worked example   target D-C

SPEC AQA SKILL

Semmelweis stated that cleaning hands before treating patients could reduce the number of infections in hospitals. The data shown are from a modern hospital where infections can sometimes still be a problem. In 2007 the hospital started a campaign to get staff to wash their hands before treating patients. Is Semmelweis's statement supported by the data? *(2 marks)*

The number of infections caught by patients has decreased each year since 2007. This partly supports Semmelweis's idea, but not completely, otherwise the number of infections would have dropped suddenly.

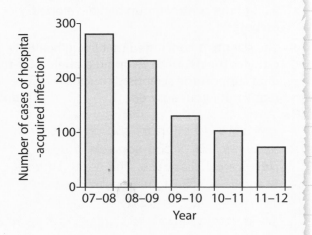

Now try this

target G-E

1 Give one way that pathogens can make us ill. *(1 mark)*

target D-C

2 Explain why Semmelweis's idea of making doctors wash their hands prevented the spread of some infections. *(2 marks)*

3 Explain why it takes some time after we are infected before we feel ill. *(2 marks)*

The immune system

The body has different ways of protecting itself against pathogens.

The IMMUNE SYSTEM helps to protect the body against pathogens. WHITE BLOOD CELLS are part of the immune system.

Some white blood cells flow round (INGEST) pathogens and destroy them.

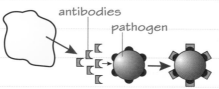

Some white blood cells produce chemical ANTIBODIES that attach to pathogens and destroy them.

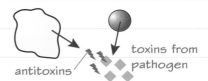

Some white blood cells produce ANTITOXINS that destroy toxins made by pathogens.

Antibodies

The antibodies produced by a white blood cell are SPECIFIC for one particular kind of pathogen. This means they can only destroy that kind of pathogen. They cannot destroy another kind of bacterium or virus.

EXAM ALERT!

Make sure you know the difference between antibody, antitoxin and antibiotic.

Students have struggled with questions like this in recent exams – **be prepared!**

Immunity

After the body has responded to an infection by a particular pathogen, the immune system remembers how to attack it. So if that kind of pathogen infects you again, your immune system responds much more quickly. You may not feel ill from the second infection – you have become IMMUNE to the pathogen.

If many people are immune to a pathogen, then it will be difficult for the pathogen to spread to people who are not immune.

Worked example

The graph shows the amount of antibody in a person's blood after infection with a particular pathogen on two separate occasions. Explain why the person did not fall ill on the second occasion. *(2 marks)*

The amount of antibody produced was much greater, and the antibodies were produced more quickly. So they destroyed the pathogens before they could cause illness.

Key:
▢ this amount of antibody kills the pathogen so quickly that you don't become ill

Amount of antibody in bloodstream (arbitrary units) — vertical axis: 0, 1, 2, 3, 4, 5, 6

first infection, second infection, immunity level

Time/weeks — horizontal axis: 0 1 2 3 4 5 6 7 8 9 10 11 12 13

Now try this

1 Name two substances produced by white blood cells that help protect us against pathogens. *(2 marks)*

2 You have recovered from an infection that causes measles. Explain why:
(a) you will not fall ill from measles again *(2 marks)*
(b) you could fall ill from a different infection, such as the pathogen that causes chickenpox. *(2 marks)*

Immunisation

IMMUNISATION means to make someone immune to a disease.

Vaccination

VACCINATION is a way of making someone immune to a disease by giving them a VACCINE. The MMR VACCINE is given to children to make them immune to measles, mumps and rubella for the rest of their lives.

A vaccine contains a small amount of a dead or inactive form of a pathogen.	The vaccine causes white blood cells to make antibodies, in the same way they would if the body was infected by live pathogens.	If the live pathogen infects you later, your immune system remembers how to destroy it, and responds quickly so you don't fall ill. You are immune.

Mutations of pathogens

A MUTATION can produce a new strain of a pathogen. The antibodies that attacked the old strain may not recognise the new strain. So people who were vaccinated against the old strain may not be immune to the new strain. The new strain may spread rapidly, causing an EPIDEMIC or PANDEMIC disease.

An epidemic is when many people catch a disease at the same time. A pandemic is when many people in many places have the same disease at the same time.

 Worked example **target D-C**

 SPEC AQA SKILL

In 2009 a flu virus normally found in pigs mutated, and was able to infect humans. An estimated 290,000 people died that year in a pandemic caused by this virus. Many of the deaths were in young adults who usually recover well from normal winter flu infections. Suggest why they were affected more seriously by the new swine flu. *(2 marks)*

Their bodies did not contain antibodies to the new swine flu, so the viruses were able to reproduce rapidly and cause death.

Risks

 SPEC AQA SKILL

A very few people suffer serious illness after receiving a vaccine such as MMR.	Many more people suffer serious illness and long-term damage from infection with the disease.	So, for most people, it is better to have the vaccination than the disease.

Now try this

 target G-E

1 A child is given a vaccine against polio.
    (a) What is in the vaccine? *(1 mark)*
    (b) Complete the following sentence: The vaccine causes the immune system to make
        .... to the pathogen, and makes the child .... to infection with polio. *(2 marks)*

target D-C

2 A parent might decide not to get their child vaccinated using the MMR vaccine.
    (a) Suggest one reason for this decision. *(1 mark)*
    (b) Suggest one reason why it would be better if their child is vaccinated. *(1 mark)*

Treating diseases

Some medicines, such as painkillers, only treat SYMPTOMS of disease. They do not kill pathogens. Other medicines help you by killing the pathogens.

Using antibiotics

- ANTIBIOTICS are medicines that kill bacterial pathogens inside the body.
- Different types of bacteria are killed by different antibiotics, so the correct antibiotic must be used.
- Deaths from bacterial diseases have greatly decreased where antibiotics are used.

A symptom is the result of disease, such as feeling pain or having a high temperature. It is not the cause of the disease.

Penicillin is an example of an antibiotic.

Antibiotic resistance

Many bacteria, including MRSA, have mutated and produced new strains that are resistant to antibiotics. They become more common as a result of natural selection. We need to avoid overuse of antibiotics to help prevent further resistance developing.

| Mutation can produce a new strain of bacteria. | → | The existing antibiotic may not affect the new strain – it is an **antibiotic-resistant strain**. | → | People who get ill with the new strain will need to be treated with a different antibiotic. | → | If there is no new antibiotic, the infection may spread rapidly and an epidemic or pandemic may occur. |

Problems with viruses

Viruses reproduce inside the cells of another organism and damage the cells. However, antibiotics do not affect viruses.

Drugs that kill viruses may also harm human cells, so viral diseases can be hard to treat.

Worked example

Use the words in the box to complete the sentences.

> antibiotics, viruses, bacteria, pathogens

Many bacterial diseases can be cured using chemicals called antibiotics.

These chemicals cannot treat diseases such as flu, which are caused by viruses. *(2 marks)*

Now try this

1 What is an antibiotic? *(1 mark)*

2 Why are antibiotic-resistant bacteria becoming more common? Tick (✓) **one** box. *(1 mark)*

Answer	Tick (✓)
Antibiotics mutate the bacteria so they become resistant.	
Natural selection due to overuse of antibiotics means only resistant bacteria survive.	
Antibiotics used on viruses make them mutate bacteria.	

7

Cultures

The action of disinfectants and antibiotics can be studied using cultures of microorganisms. Other microorganisms from the air and surfaces can easily contaminate cultures when they are being prepared. Several techniques can help prevent this.

 Sterilising dishes and culture media

STERILISATION kills microorganisms.

- Petri dishes can be sterilised by autoclaving or heating to a high temperature.

- Culture media (the substance that the microorganisms grow on, such as nutrient agar) are sterilised by heating to a high temperature.

> Microorganisms grow in a culture medium. More than one medium is referred to as **media**.

 Sterilising inoculating loops

The loop is sterilised in a hot flame and then cooled, before using it to transfer microorganisms to the growth medium.

 Sealing Petri dishes

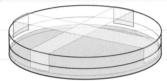

The lid is secured to the dish with adhesive tape to stop microorganisms from the air getting in.

Worked example   **target G-E**

Cultures of microorganisms should be incubated at a maximum temperature of 25°C in school and college laboratories. Explain why.
(2 marks)

Temperatures higher than this encourage rapid growth in bacteria. This includes pathogenic bacteria that are harmful to humans.

When microorganisms are grown in industry, they are cultured at higher temperatures than 25°C because they are not handled by people. The microorganisms grow more quickly at these higher temperatures, but there is no risk that people will get infected by the bacteria.

Now try this

 target G-E

1 Why are high temperatures used in several stages of the preparation of bacterial cultures? *(1 mark)*

2 Explain why industrial cultures of microorganisms can safely be grown at higher temperatures than cultures grown in a school lab. *(2 marks)*

 target D-C

3 Give three ways in which cultures of microorganisms can easily be contaminated with other microorganisms during preparation. *(3 marks)*

Biology six mark question 1

There will be one 6 mark question on your exam paper which will be marked for *Quality of Written Communication* as well as scientific knowledge. This means that you need to apply your scientific knowledge, present your answer in a logical and organised way and make sure that your spelling, grammar and punctuation are as good as you can make them.

Worked example

There are many vaccinations that can be given to young children. A few years ago the number of children being vaccinated with the MMR vaccine fell because one doctor had suggested that the vaccine could cause children to develop autism. Explain why it is important for parents to get their children vaccinated. *(6 marks)*

Vaccination makes you immune to the disease. So if the child is vaccinated, it won't ever be able to catch the disease.

If the child caught the disease, they would have a much greater chance of being very ill. So it's much better to be vaccinated. If most children are vaccinated then the disease won't be able to spread easily.

EXAM ALERT!

Always plan what you are going to write for the six-mark questions. You are given credit for a well-organised answer.

Students have struggled with questions like this in recent exams – **be prepared!**

Command words

The COMMAND WORD in this question is 'explain'. This means that you need say WHAT is happening and WHY.

This part of the answer is not complete because it doesn't describe how vaccination produces immunity – by stimulating the immune system to produce antibodies, which leads to the development of immunity.

This part of the answer could be even better if it said more clearly that although there is a very small risk of harm from a vaccination, there is a much greater risk of harm if you catch the disease.

Now try this

Explain how a balanced diet and regular exercise can help you stay healthy. *(6 marks)*

Receptors

Humans react to their surroundings using their nervous system.

stimulus change in surroundings	→	nervous system detects stimuli and coordinates response	→	response change in organism's behaviour as a result of stimulus

> Note the spelling:
one **stimulus**, two
or more **stimuli**.

Cells that detect stimuli are called RECEPTORS. Receptor cells in different organs of the body respond to different kinds of stimuli.

Receptor organs	Contain cells sensitive to ...
eye	• light
ear	• change in position (helps us balance) • sound
nose	• chemicals in air (smell)
tongue	• chemicals in solids and liquids (taste)
skin (different cells for each stimulus)	• touch, pressure, pain, temperature

An **organ** contains different groups of cells that work together for a particular purpose.

Worked example

target G-E

The diagram shows a light receptor cell from a human eye, labelled to show three cell structures that are also found in most other animal cells.

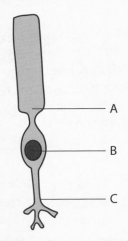

A
B
C

Which row in the table shows the names of these structures? Tick (✓) one box. *(1 mark)*

Cell structures			Tick (✓)
cell wall	nucleus	cytoplasm	
cell membrane	nucleus	cytoplasm	✓
cell membrane	nucleus	chloroplast	

Now try this

target G-E

1 Where in the human body are the cells that respond to sound? *(1 mark)*

2 A girl puts her hand on a sharp pin and quickly moves her hand away again.
   (a) Identify the stimulus and response in this example. *(2 marks)*
   (b) What kind of receptors in the girl's body received the stimulus? *(1 mark)*

Responses

Nerves contain nerve cells (NEURONES) that connect the CENTRAL NERVOUS SYSTEM (spinal cord and brain) to receptors and EFFECTORS. The brain coordinates the response by different effectors.

REFLEX ACTIONS are automatic responses that are very fast and do not involve conscious thought. They involve only two or three neurones of different types.

(1) A receptor cell responds to a stimulus by producing an electrical IMPULSE.

(2) The impulse passes from the receptor along a SENSORY NEURONE to the central nervous system.

(3) The impulse passes from the sensory neurone to a RELAY NEURONE in the central nervous system.

(4) The impulse passes from the relay neurone to a MOTOR NEURONE.

(5) The impulse passes along the motor neurone to the EFFECTOR.

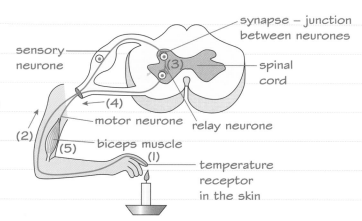

Effectors are:
- muscles that respond by contracting
- glands that respond by **secreting** (releasing) chemicals, e.g. hormones.

Synapses

The junction between two neurones is called a SYNAPSE. Electrical impulses cannot cross synapses. Instead, a chemical crosses the synapse to the next neurone.

Worked example target G-E

Fill in the gaps to complete the sentences below.

The <u>electrical</u> impulse in the first neurone triggers the release of a <u>chemical</u> into the gap in the synapse. The <u>chemical</u> crosses the gap and triggers an <u>electrical</u> impulse in the next neurone.

EXAM ALERT!

Remember that nerves and neurones are not the same. Nerves are collections of neurones. Also, neurones carry electrical impulses, not messages.

Students have struggled with questions like this in recent exams – **be prepared!**

Now try this

 target G-E

1 Name the point where two nerve cells meet.
(1 mark)

2 Name the kind of neurone that links the spinal cord to a muscle cell. *(1 mark)*

 target D-C

3 Describe the role of the three different neurones in a reflex arc. *(3 marks)*

Controlling internal conditions

Internal conditions in the body are controlled so that the body works properly.

Water content

Ion content

water is lost from:
- lungs when we breathe out
- skin in sweat, to cool us down
- kidneys in URINE

ions are lost from:
- skin in sweat
- kidneys in urine

Water and ions are taken into the body in food and drink.

Worked example target D-C

Body temperature and blood sugar concentration are two other conditions that are controlled in the body. Explain why they are controlled. *(2 marks)*

Body temperature is controlled to keep the body at a temperature at which enzymes work best.

Blood sugar concentration is controlled so that cells are provided with a constant supply of energy.

Hormones

Many processes in the body are controlled by chemicals called HORMONES.

Hormones are **secreted** (released) by a **gland** into the blood.	→	Hormones are transported around the body in the blood.	→	Hormones cause response from a **target organ**.

Now try this

 target G-E

1 State two ways in which water is lost from the body. *(2 marks)*

2 State one way in which ions are lost from the body. *(1 mark)*

 target D-C

3 Name a hormone in the human body, the gland where it is produced and its target organ. *(3 marks)*

The menstrual cycle

The MENSTRUAL CYCLE in women is controlled by several hormones. They cause the MATURATION (ripening) and release of eggs from the ovaries, and cause changes in the thickness of the womb lining.

Three hormones control the release of an egg each month.

You won't be expected to know details of the menstrual cycle, just the roles of the hormones.

OESTROGEN inhibits (prevents) further production of FSH so no more eggs mature this month

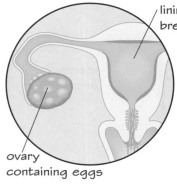

lining of womb breaks down

ovary containing eggs

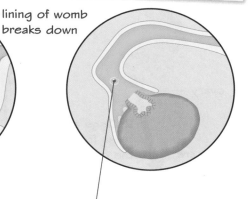

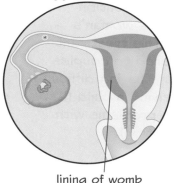

lining of womb gets thicker

FOLLICLE-STIMULATING HORMONE (FSH)
• causes eggs in ovaries to mature
• stimulates ovaries to produce hormones including oestrogen

LUTEINISING HORMONE (LH)
• causes an ovary to release an egg

FSH and LH are secreted by the pituitary gland below the brain. Oestrogen is secreted by the ovaries.

Oral contraceptives

ORAL CONTRACEPTIVES are 'birth control' pills, as they help to prevent pregnancy. They contain hormones that inhibit the release of FSH, which means:

• no eggs mature

• so no eggs are ready to be released from an ovary.

Oral contraceptives may contain the hormones OESTROGEN and PROGESTERONE.

Worked example

The first contraceptive pills contained much higher doses of oestrogen than modern pills, and some modern pills contain only progesterone. State why the amounts and type of hormone were changed.   *(1 mark)*

Large amounts of oestrogen caused side effects in the women who took them. The newer pills cause fewer side effects but are still effective.

1 (a) Name three hormones involved in the menstrual cycle.   *(3 marks)*

(b) State where each of the hormones in your answer to **(a)** is produced.   *(3 marks)*

2 Why are the hormones progesterone and oestrogen used in oral contraceptive pills?   *(3 marks)*

Increasing fertility

FERTILITY is the ability to have children.
- Contraceptive pills reduce fertility.
- Fertility drugs can increase fertility.

Fertility drugs

FERTILITY DRUGS contain the hormones FSH and LH. The drugs can help women who produce too little FSH by stimulating eggs to mature and then be released.

IVF (in vitro fertilisation)

IVF is fertilisation outside a woman's body. This treatment is offered to couples who are having difficulty conceiving a child (i.e. having problems with fertilisation).

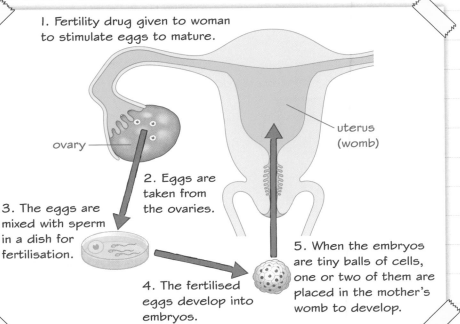

1. Fertility drug given to woman to stimulate eggs to mature.

ovary

uterus (womb)

2. Eggs are taken from the ovaries.

3. The eggs are mixed with sperm in a dish for fertilisation.

4. The fertilised eggs develop into embryos.

5. When the embryos are tiny balls of cells, one or two of them are placed in the mother's womb to develop.

Worked example

target D–C

SPEC AQA SKILL

A couple have been offered IVF treatment. Here are some pieces of information they are given:
- IVF increases the chance of being able to have a child.
- IVF often results in multiple births.
- Twins and triplets mean a higher risk of a difficult birth.
- IVF involves injecting several different drugs, often daily for a few weeks.

(a) Give **one** advantage of having IVF treatment. *(1 mark)*

(b) Give **one** disadvantage of IVF. *(1 mark)*

(a) The couple are more likely to have a child.

(b) Giving birth to twins might be riskier for the mother.

Now try this

target G–E

1 Explain what fertility drugs contain that helps them to increase fertility. *(2 marks)*

2 What is **in vitro fertilisation?** *(1 mark)*

target D–C

3 Describe how IVF can make it possible for a couple to have a baby when the woman doesn't normally release matured eggs from her ovaries. *(4 marks)*

There are other possible answers for this from the information in the question.

Plant responses

Plants respond to changes in light, moisture and gravity by changing how they grow.

- Growth in response to light is called PHOTOTROPISM.
- Growth in response to gravity is called GRAVITROPISM.

Gravitropism is sometimes called **geotropism**. You can use either word in the exam.

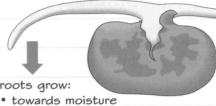

shoots grow:
- towards light
- against gravity

roots grow:
- towards moisture
- in the direction of gravity

Plant hormones

Plants produce hormones that coordinate and control growth.

AUXIN is the plant hormone that controls phototropism and geotropism. Cells in plant shoots that contain more auxin ELONGATE (get longer) more than cells with less auxin. This causes UNEQUAL GROWTH RATES in cells in shoots.

Auxin is producd in the shoot or root tip, then moves away from the tip to where it affects cells.

Auxin and gravitropism

Auxin has a <u>different effect</u> in plant root cells. It INHIBITS (reduces) elongation.

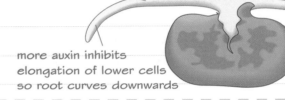

gravity causes auxin to move to lower part of root

more auxin inhibits elongation of lower cells so root curves downwards

---

Worked example   target D-C

This shoot is growing towards light as a result of phototropism. Explain what is happening to auxin at point A, and to the cells at point B.

(3 marks)

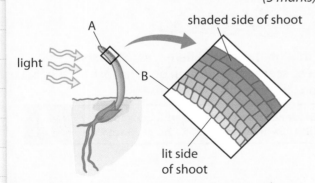

shaded side of shoot

light

A

B

lit side of shoot

At A, light is causing the auxin to move to the shaded side of the shoot. At B, cells on the shaded side contain more auxin than cells on the lit side. So the cells of the shaded side grow longer and the shoot grows towards the light.

EXAM ALERT!

Remember: auxin causes cells in plant stems to get longer, but causes root cells to grow more slowly.

Students have struggled with questions like this in recent exams – **be prepared!**

Now try this

target G-E

1   What is **phototropism**?   *(1 mark)*

2   Compare the responses of plant shoot cells and root cells to auxin.   *(2 marks)*

target D-C

3   Describe how unequal distribution of auxin causes a horizontal root to start growing downwards.

(3 marks)

Plant hormones

Plant growth hormones can be used in:

- AGRICULTURE (growing crop plants in fields)
- HORTICULTURE (growing flowers, fruit and vegetable plants).

Weedkillers (herbicides)

WEEDS are plants that grow where we don't want them. Plant hormones are used in SELECTIVE WEEDKILLERS. These kill broad-leaved weeds in grass lawns and in crops that have narrow leaves, such as wheat. Killing the weeds in crops reduces competition for water and nutrients in the soil.

The hormones in the weedkiller affect the weeds so that they die, but don't harm the grass.

Rooting hormones

Plant hormones are used in ROOTING POWDER. If the stem of a plant cutting is dipped in the powder, the stem will develop roots more quickly.

The diagram shows two germinating maize seeds. The seeds have been kept in identical conditions, apart from the amount of hormone in the water they were given.

Compare the seedling roots, and explain whether you think rooting powder produces better roots.   *(3 marks)*

grown in pure water   grown in water containing hormone

maize seeds

roots

The root of the seed grown with hormone is longer than the one with no hormone. I think that the hormone increases rate of root growth, because that was the only difference in the way the seeds were kept.

EXAM ALERT!

Although there are differences in the shoots of these seeds, the question does not ask for this. So don't include this in your answer.

Students have struggled with questions like this in recent exams – **be prepared!**

1 State two uses of plant hormones in agriculture and horticulture.   *(2 marks)*

2 Explain why plant cuttings dipped in rooting powder develop roots more quickly than if rooting powder is not used.   *(2 marks)*

3 Explain why farmers use hormone weedkillers on their crops.   *(2 marks)*

New drugs

DRUGS are chemicals that affect how the body works. Scientists are continually developing new drugs. New MEDICAL DRUGS must be extensively tested before doctors can PRESCRIBE them to patients. There are several stages of testing.

 In the laboratory

Drugs are tested on:

cultures of cells

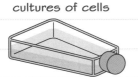

cultures of tissues

animals

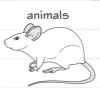

These MODELS help predict how the drugs may behave in the human body.

 Clinical trials: stage 1

healthy volunteer

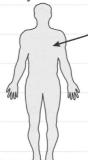

very small DOSE of drug

To check that the drug is not TOXIC (harmful).

Medical drugs are prescribed (given) by doctors to help patients who are ill.

 Clinical trials: stage 2

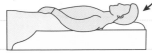

different doses of drug

patient with the disease that the new drug is developed for

To test EFFICACY (whether it works) and to find the OPTIMUM dose (the dose that works best).

Placebos

In some trials, some of the patients are given a PLACEBO. This is something that looks like the drug but doesn't contain the drug.

Results from patients who took the placebo are compared with results from patients who had the drug. Any difference suggests how well the drug works.

Worked example target D-C

In a double-blind trial for a new drug, neither the doctor nor the patient know whether the patient has been give the drug or a placebo until after the trial has finished. Explain why.   *(2 marks)*

 Double-blind because two people (doctor and patient) don't know.

The patient might be happier about taking the drug rather than the placebo, and this can affect the results. If the doctor does not know what the patient took, they will be more objective about the results.

Now try this

 target G-E

1 What is a placebo?   *(1 mark)*
2 Describe three stages of drug testing.   *(3 marks)*

 target D-C

3 Give three reasons why new drugs need to be fully tested before doctors can prescribe them to patients.   *(3 marks)*

Thalidomide and Statins

Thalidomide and statins are medical drugs.

Using thalidomide

THALIDOMIDE is a drug that caused a lot of problems when it was first prescribed by doctors.

| developed as a sleeping pill | → | also used to control morning sickness in pregnant women | → | caused severe limb abnormalities in babies born to many of the women who took the drug | → | thalidomide was then banned |

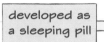 not tested on pregnant women

As a result of the problems with thalidomide, drug testing has been made more thorough.

Thalidomide is now used successfully to treat diseases such as **leprosy**.

Using statins

STATINS are drugs that are prescribed to patients with high blood cholesterol. Statins help reduce the level of blood cholesterol, which can reduce the risk of developing CARDIOVASCULAR DISEASES.

EXAM ALERT!

In a question like this, use the information given in the question to help you give reasons.

Students have struggled with questions like this in recent exams – **be prepared!**

Worked example   target D-C

 SPEC AQA SKILL

A major study was carried out on the effectiveness of statins on patients with cardiovascular disease. 2223 patients were given a placebo and 2221 were treated with statins. After about 5 years there were 30% fewer deaths from heart disease in the statin group compared with the control group.

Should the National Health Service give permission to doctors to prescribe statins? Give the reasons for your answer.   *(2 marks)*

There were 30% fewer deaths over 5 years when people used the statins compared to people not taking the drug. This is a big saving in lives and cost to the Health Service. So it seems a good idea for the doctors to prescribe statins to protect against cardiovascular disease.

Cardiovascular diseases are diseases of the heart and circulatory system.

Now try this

1 (a) What was thalidomide first developed for?   *(1 mark)*

  (b) What is thalidomide now used successfully for?   *(1 mark)*

target G-E

2 Complete the following sentences.
Statins are one type of ....
They are used to lower the risk of ....   *(2 marks)*

target D-C

3 Explain why the effect of thalidomide on babies was not expected.   *(2 marks)*

Recreational drugs

A RECREATIONAL DRUG is a drug that people use for personal satisfaction rather than for medical purposes.

Recreational drugs

Legal drugs
(allowed by law)
e.g.
- alcohol
- nicotine (in tobacco)

Illegal drugs
(forbidden by law)
e.g.
- ecstasy
- cannabis
- heroin

Smoking tobacco and drinking too much alcohol can lead to many health problems.

These drugs can harm the heart and circulatory system.

Cannabis

Cannabis is a drug that is usually burned and the smoke inhaled. The smoke contains many chemicals. Some of these chemicals may cause MENTAL ILLNESS in some of the people who use cannabis, particularly if they are regular users while still teenagers.

Addiction

Some drugs, such as heroin and cocaine, are very ADDICTIVE. This means they change chemical processes in the body, and make the person DEPENDENT on taking the drug. They may need more and more of the drug to have the same effect. If the person stops taking the drug, they suffer distressing WITHDRAWAL SYMPTOMS.

Worked example D-C

 SPEC AQA SKILL

Some people who take illegal 'soft' drugs, such as cannabis, progress to taking 'harder' illegal drugs such as heroin. Suggest one reason for this. *(1 mark)*

They may get used to the effect of the soft drugs and want to try something that has a bigger effect.

Remember that drugs alter chemical processes in the body. They do not cause withdrawal symptoms directly.

Other possible answers are:
- They may like taking risks and the harder drugs are bigger risks.
- Buying illegal soft drugs may give them access to illegal hard drugs, which will tempt them to try the hard drugs.

Now try this

 target G-E

1 Name one legal recreational drug and one illegal recreational drug. *(2 marks)*
2 Give one way that using cannabis can harm the body. *(1 mark)*

 target D-C

3 Explain why heroin users find it difficult to stop taking the drug. *(2 marks)*

Drugs and health

Drugs affect the body in many ways. Some of these effects are harmful.

 Evaluating prescribed drugs

Medical drugs help people with particular illnesses or conditions get better or reduce their symptoms. These drugs may also have SIDE EFFECTS that are harmful. A doctor has to evaluate the benefits and risks of the patient taking the drug. The doctor will only prescribe a drug if they decide that the benefits will be much greater than the risks.

EVALUATION:

BENEFITS:
• cure illness?
• relieve symptoms?
• better quality of life?

which are greater: benefits or risks?

RISKS:
• problems caused by side effects?

Doctors may need to evaluate the use of different drugs and treatments for the same illness, to decide which is best for a patient.

 Evaluating recreational drugs

People have to evaluate the risks and benefits of taking recreational drugs. This may mean making a choice between a short-term benefit and the risk of harm later.

✓ Short-term benefit of drinking alcohol: it makes some people feel happier.

✗ UK 2012: nearly 9,000 deaths caused by drinking too much alcohol (not including alcohol-related accidents).

Worked example

 Many more people are treated in hospital for the effects of smoking and misuse of alcohol than for the use of illegal drugs.
Explain why. *(2 marks)*

There are many more people who smoke or misuse alcohol than people who take illegal drugs. So there will be more who suffer harm from tobacco and alcohol than suffer harm from illegal drugs.

This doesn't mean that illegal drugs are safer to use than legal (prescribed and non-prescribed) drugs. The **proportion** of illegal drug users who suffer harm is greater than the proportion of legal drug users who suffer harm.

Now try this

 1 Why can medical drugs cause harm as well as help people who are ill? *(1 mark)*

 2 (a) Alcohol is a recreational drug. Give one reason why it is classified as a legal drug. *(1 mark)*

(b) Give one reason why alcohol can be a problem. *(1 mark)*

Drugs in sport

Some types of drugs can affect sporting performance.

STIMULANTS increase the rate of body functions, such as heart rate

A faster heart rate delivers oxygen and sugars to muscles more quickly, so they can release more energy more quickly.

ANABOLIC STEROIDS stimulate muscle growth.

Bigger muscles can help move bigger weights and generate more power, e.g. in weightlifting.

Drug bans in sport

Use of drugs to improve performance in sports competition is considered UNETHICAL.

Reasons for this include:

- side effects of the drugs can harm athletes
- may give unfair advantage over athletes who don't use drugs.

Some drugs that affect performance are legal and some can be prescribed, but all are banned by sports competition regulations.

Ethical questions are about what people think is right or wrong. In a question about ethical issues, you may need to explain why different people have different ideas about what is right or wrong.

Worked example   **D-C**

The graph shows the effect of injecting different doses of testosterone (a steroid) on 60 men who were weight training for 20 weeks. Use information from the graph to explain why testosterone is a banned drug in sports.   *(2 marks)*

The graph shows that higher doses of testosterone increase the amount of weight that the leg muscle can lift. This could give an athlete an unfair advantage over athletes who haven't used testosterone.

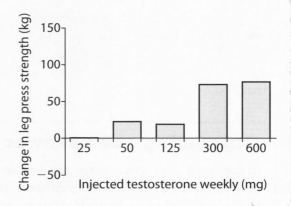

Now try this

1 Name one group of drugs that could improve sporting performance.   *(1 mark)*

2 Give one reason why drug use is banned in sporting competitions.   *(1 mark)*

3 Explain why stimulants can improve sporting performance.   *(2 marks)*

Biology six mark question 2

There will be one 6 mark question on your exam paper which will be marked for *Quality of Written Communication* as well as scientific knowledge. This means that you need to apply your scientific knowledge, present your answer in a logical and organised way and make sure that your spelling, grammar and punctuation are as good as you can make them.

Worked example

Describe how new medical drugs are tested and explain why each stage of testing is needed.

(6 marks)

New drugs are first tested in the laboratory. They are tested on cells, tissues and live animals. This is to make sure they work properly.

If the first tests are successful, the drug is then tested in very low doses on healthy people to make sure the drug doesn't harm them.

Then the drug is tested on patients who have the disease that the drug is being developed to treat. The dose is increased to find the optimum dose, which has the best effect on the patient's illness. These tests may be double-blind trials using a placebo to make sure they are fair tests.

This part of the answer could have been made much clearer by explaining what 'properly' means. For example, it could have said that the drug is tested to make sure it has the effect that doctors intend, and to make sure that the drug is not toxic (poisonous).

A better answer would have explained that a double-blind trial means the doctor and patient don't know whether the patient has had the new drug or a placebo, which looks just like the drug but contains no drug. A double-blind trial means that the patient can't be affected by how they feel about getting either the drug or placebo, and that doctors are more objective about analysing the results.

Organising your answer

Make sure you write your answer in a LOGICAL ORDER. There is often more than one way to organise an answer, and it does not matter which way you choose, as long as it is clear.

Now try this

1 Describe how hormones are used in contraceptives and fertility treatments to control fertility.

(6 marks)

Competition

Organisms need a supply of materials from their surroundings, and sometimes from other living organisms, so that they can survive and reproduce. This means there is COMPETITION between organisms for materials that are in limited supply.

Competition between plants

competition for light and space

competition for water and nutrients

Competition between animals

Animals may compete with each other for:

- food
- mates for reproduction
- TERRITORY (space for feeding, reproduction and rearing young).

You will be expected to know the factors that organisms are competing for in an example.

Worked example   D-C

In spring, a male robin will sing loudly. Explain the role of singing in robins in terms of competition. *(2 marks)*

A male robin competes with other male robins for mates (females) and for territory. Singing loudly warns other males to keep out of the robin's territory and attracts females who choose to mate with him.

EXAM ALERT!

Make sure that you know what the command words mean. **Explain** means give a reason why. **Suggest** means you need to apply your knowledge to a new situation. **Describe** means say what is happening.

Students have struggled with questions like this in recent exams – **be prepared!**

Deterring predators

Many organisms are the food of other organisms. Some animals and plants have special features that deter PREDATORS.

Some animals advertise that they are poisonous with very bright colours.

Some animals use colours to make them look more frightening, like these big 'eyes'.

Some plants have big thorns.

Other plants are poisonous.

Now try this

G-E

1 Which three of the environmental factors shown in the table do animals compete with other animals for? Tick (✓) three boxes. *(3 marks)*

2 Describe one way in which a small animal might frighten off a large predator. *(1 mark)*

D-C

3 A farmer plants the seeds of his crop plants so that they are well separated from each other. Explain why. *(2 marks)*

Environmental factors	Tick (✓)
food	
light	
territory	
mates	
warmth	

Adaptations

All organisms (including microorganisms) have ADAPTATIONS that help them survive the conditions of the environment in which they normally live.

Animals in the Arctic

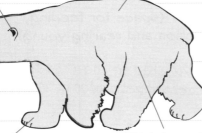

Small ears (reduced surface area) – less heat loss to air.

White colour for CAMOUFLAGE against snow.

Large feet for better grip on ice and stop bear sinking into snow.

Thick fur and fat below skin INSULATE (reduce rate of heat loss).

Animals in dry environments

Camels:

- have a hump of fat that is a food store; fat also releases water as a result of respiration
- can drink large quantities of water at a time
- have a thick coat at the top of the body that insulates against heat from Sun.

Dry environments can also be very hot. African elephants have:

- large ears to transfer body heat to air quickly.

Worked example

target D-C

 Label the diagram to describe how the listed adaptations help a cactus to survive in a dry environment.

(3 marks)

The cactus has no leaves which reduces water loss to air, but its green body still allows photosynthesis to take place.

Thick fleshy body stores water inside for times of drought.

Large root system collects as much water as possible from underground.

Extreme environments

Extreme environments have extreme conditions, for example:

- high levels of salt, e.g. a saltmarsh
- high temperatures, e.g. volcanic hot springs
- high pressures, e.g. the deep ocean.

Extremophiles

EXTREMOPHILES are organisms that have adaptations so they can TOLERATE very extreme environments. Many extremophiles are microorganisms.

Now try this

 target G-E

1 Give one adaptation of a polar bear to living in a cold environment. *(1 mark)*

2 Scientists are investigating the adaptations of microorganisms from a volcanic hot spring. What do these adaptations help the microorganisms to tolerate? *(1 mark)*

 target D-C

3 Describe how the adaptation in your answer to question **1** helps the polar bear to survive. *(1 mark)*

Indicators

Factors in the environment affect living organisms and their DISTRIBUTION (how widely spread they are). Changes in these factors may change their distribution.

environmental factors

living factors, e.g.
• prey
• competitor
• predator

non-living factors, e.g.
• light
• average temperature
• average rainfall
• oxygen levels in water
• pollution

Changes in these factors can affect organisms. For example, if there is a change in average temperature or rainfall this may change the distribution of organisms in an area.

Oxygen levels are high in unpolluted water and low in polluted water.

Changes in non-living factors can be measured using equipment, e.g. oxygen meter, thermometer, rainfall gauge.

Pollution indicators

Some species can be used as INDICATORS of pollution in air or in water.

This LICHEN species indicates lots of air pollution, e.g. high sulfur dioxide concentration in air.

This lichen species indicates no air pollution, e.g. no sulfur dioxide in air.

Bloodworms indicate highly polluted water.

Mayfly larvae indicate unpolluted water.

Worked example | **target D-C**

 SPEC AQA SKILL

The table shows the results of lichen surveys at the same place in two different years. Air samples from the same site showed that air quality had improved between 1975 and 2010. Do the lichen data support this conclusion? Give a reason for your answer. *(3 marks)*

	Number of lichens found on 5 trees	
Survey year	1975	2010
Lichens tolerant of high pollution	35	22
Lichens intolerant of high pollution	1	24

The numbers of lichens intolerant of high pollution increased by 230% between 1975 and 2010, and the numbers of lichens tolerant of high pollution decreased by 37% during this time. These results suggest that the level of air pollution in this place decreased between 1975 and 2010.

Now try this

 target G-E

1 What is meant by the distribution of an organism?
(1 mark)

 target D-C

2 Describe how invertebrate animals are used as water pollution indicators. *(2 marks)*

3 Name one non-living factor that could be measured to indicate water pollution, and describe how its level changes with pollution. *(2 marks)*

Energy and biomass

The source of energy for most food chains is light energy from the Sun.

light energy from Sun → small amount of energy captured by green plants and algae

light energy transferred to chemical energy — **photosynthesis** → chemical energy stored in substances in cells and tissues

mass of living material = BIOMASS

Pyramids of biomass

The biomass of organisms at different levels of a food chain can be shown in a PYRAMID OF BIOMASS.

The table shows the biomass of organisms in the food chain:

lettuce → caterpillar → thrush

Use the data in the table to draw a pyramid of biomass. *(3 marks)*

Organism	Biomass (g/m²)
lettuce	120
caterpillar	60
thrush	12

Draw your diagram on graph paper. Make sure the width of each bar is drawn to scale.

The bars are always in the same order: start at the bottom of the food chain, working along the food chain as you move to the top of the pyramid.

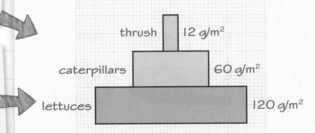

thrush 12 g/m²
caterpillars 60 g/m²
lettuces 120 g/m²

Complete the sentences to explain the shape of a pyramid of biomass. *(3 marks)*

Some energy from <u>respiration</u> is lost to the environment as <u>heat</u> energy.

In animals, some materials and energy are lost to the environment in the <u>waste</u> they produce.

So there is less biomass in each level as you move <u>up</u> the pyramid.

Remember that energy and biomass are not the same thing. Biomass is broken down in respiration, releasing carbon dioxide, and some of the energy released from respiration is heat energy.

 G-E

1 Which process in green plants and algae uses light energy? *(1 mark)*

 D-C

2 A rabbit eats 500 g of grass. Explain why the rabbit will not increase in biomass by 500 g. *(2 marks)*

Decay

There is a constant cycling of materials between living organisms and the environment. In a STABLE (unchanging) community, the amount of materials removed from the environment is balanced by the amount returned by decay.

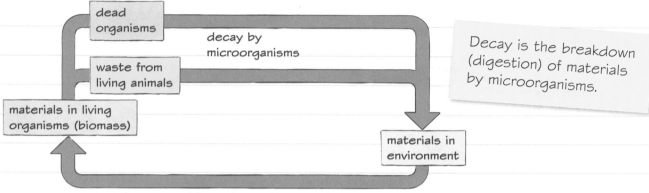

Decay is the breakdown (digestion) of materials by microorganisms.

Recycling kitchen and garden waste

Garden and kitchen waste can be used to make COMPOST, either in the garden or by council schemes. Conditions in the compost should be controlled to encourage the growth of decay microorganisms, which grow and digest faster in conditions that are:

• moist   • warm   • aerobic (oxygen present).

Worked example

The graph shows the amount of household waste collected by a council for some of the years between 2000 and 2012. It also shows how the waste was disposed of. The council's aim was to reduce the amount of waste sent to landfill.

Use the graph to help you explain how composting has helped the council to achieve its aim.

(2 marks)

The proportion of the waste sent for composting has increased each year. This means that less waste is left to go to landfill.

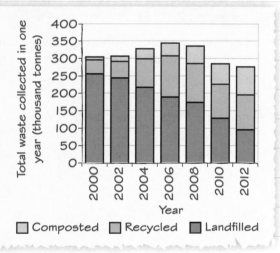

Now try this

1 What is meant by 'decay'?   *(2 marks)*

2 Why do compost heaps produce compost fastest in sunny places?   *(1 mark)*

3 If a gardener grows crops in the same piece of ground each year, without adding compost, the yield (amount of food) he gets from the crops gets less and less. Explain why.   *(2 marks)*

Carbon cycling

The constant cycling of carbon between the air and living organisms is called the CARBON CYCLE.

Combustion is burning.

Detritus feeders are animals that eat dead and decaying material, e.g. earthworms.

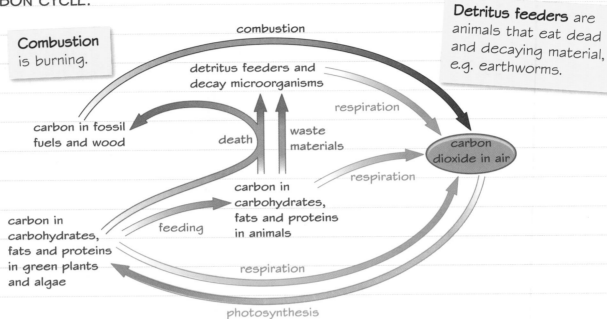

combustion

detritus feeders and decay microorganisms

respiration

carbon in fossil fuels and wood

death

waste materials

respiration

carbon dioxide in air

carbon in carbohydrates, fats and proteins in animals

carbon in carbohydrates, fats and proteins in green plants and algae

feeding

respiration

photosynthesis

By the time the microorganisms and detritus feeders have broken down the waste products and dead bodies of organisms, and cycled the materials as plant nutrients, all the energy originally absorbed by green plants and algae has been transferred.

Worked example D-C

Compare the roles of photosynthesis, respiration and combustion in the carbon cycle. *(3 marks)*

Photosynthesis is the process in which carbon dioxide is removed from the air and converted into carbon compounds in green plants and algae.

Respiration is the process that releases carbon dioxide from living organisms back into the air.

Combustion is the process that releases carbon dioxide from dead organisms back into the air.

EXAM ALERT!

Remember that plants photosynthesise but they also respire 24 hours a day. Microbes respire too.

Students have struggled with questions like this in recent exams – **be prepared!**

Now try this

 target G-E

1 Name one process that releases carbon dioxide into the air. *(1 mark)*

2 Name one type of molecule in living organisms that contains carbon. *(1 mark)*

 target D-C

3 Describe how carbon in animal waste is returned to the air. *(2 marks)*

Genes

Genes, chromosomes and nucleus

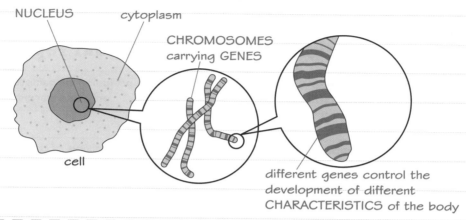

NUCLEUS   cytoplasm

CHROMOSOMES carrying GENES

different genes control the development of different CHARACTERISTICS of the body

cell

Worked example target G-E

Explain why individual plants and animals have characteristics similar to their parents. Use the words from the box to complete the sentences.
(3 marks)

cells	characteristic	fertilisation
	genes	growth

A plant or animal inherits genes from its parents during fertilisation , when sex cells (gametes) from each parent fuse. Each of their genes controls the development of a particular characteristic . So the offspring are similar to their parents because they have copies of some of their parents' genes .

Causes of differences

differences between individuals of the same kind

Note: most variations are caused by a combination of genes and environment.

caused by differences in genes they have inherited, e.g. eye colour (GENETIC CAUSES)

combination of both causes e.g. weight, skin colour

caused by differences in conditions in which they developed, e.g. riding a bike, scars (ENVIRONMENTAL CAUSES)

Now try this

 target G-E

1 In which of the cell structures shown in the table are genes found? Tick (✓) one box.   *(1 mark)*

Cell structures	Tick (✓)
cytoplasm	
cell membrane	
nucleus	

 target D-C

2 Name two different causes of differences in characteristics in dogs.   *(2 marks)*

Reproduction

REPRODUCTION is the production of new individuals. There are two forms of reproduction.

 1 Sexual reproduction

| gamete from mother fuses (joins) with gamete from father |
| ↓ |
| mixes genetic information from each parent |
| ↓ |
| offspring have different combinations of genes, so show variety in characteristics |

 2 Asexual reproduction

| no fusion of gametes – only one parent |
| ↓ |
| no mixing of genetic information |
| ↓ |
| all offspring have same genes as parent and each other |

 Worked example **G-E**

Tick (✓) the correct box to show which form of reproduction produces clones.

Form of reproduction	Tick (✓)
sexual	
asexual	✓

 Clones are individuals with identical genes.

Taking plant cuttings

New plants can be produced quickly and cheaply, by taking cuttings from an older plant.

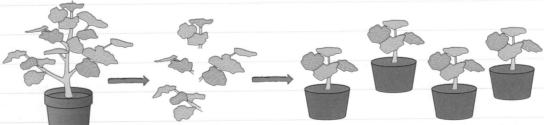

several cuttings taken from parent plant

cuttings grown into new plants that are genetically identical (clones)

Now try this

 G-E

1 How many parents does a plant have if it was produced by:
(a) asexual reproduction   (1 mark)
(b) sexual reproduction?   (1 mark)

2 Which form of reproduction involves gametes?   (1 mark)

 D-C

3 Explain why plants grown from cuttings from the same plant are clones.   (2 marks)

Cloning

There are several modern techniques for cloning organisms.

 ## Tissue culture

Plant tissue culture is like taking plant cuttings, but with very small pieces that contain just a few plant cells. The new plants are all clones because their cells contain the same genes as the parent plant.

 ## Embryo transplants

Splitting embryos makes it possible to produce small numbers of clone animals at the same time. This is most often done with high-quality farm animals.

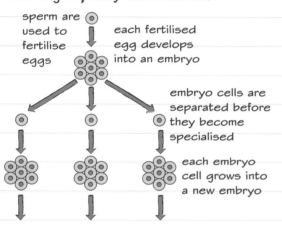

sperm are used to fertilise eggs

each fertilised egg develops into an embryo

embryo cells are separated before they become specialised

each embryo cell grows into a new embryo

- all the offspring are genetically identical (clones)
- each embryo is placed in the womb (uterus) of a different SURROGATE MOTHER to develop until ready for birth

 ## Adult cell cloning

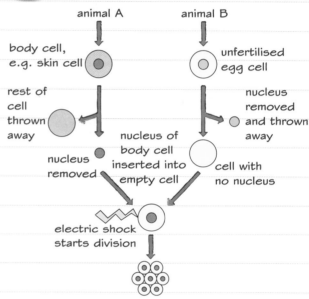

animal A   animal B

body cell, e.g. skin cell

unfertilised egg cell

rest of cell thrown away

nucleus removed and thrown away

nucleus removed

nucleus of body cell inserted into empty cell

cell with no nucleus

electric shock starts division

- cell divides to form embryo
- embryo inserted into womb of adult female C to develop until birth

---

In the diagram shown above right, will the animal that is born be a clone of animal A, animal B or the adult female C in whose womb it developed? Explain your answer.   *(2 marks)*

Animal A. It has the same genes because the nucleus in the egg was taken from the cell of animal A.

 Now try this

 G-E

1   Name one technique for cloning animals.   *(1 mark)*

 D-C

2   Describe one way in which plant tissue culture and taking plant cuttings are:
(a) similar, **(b)** different.   *(2 marks)*

3   Describe the role of each of the three adult animals used in the development of a cloned offspring by adult cell cloning.   *(3 marks)*

Genetic engineering

Genetic engineering produces GENETICALLY MODIFIED (GM) organisms.

GENETIC ENGINEERING is the transfer of a gene from one organism to a different organism so that the desired characteristic is produced in that organism.

The jellyfish has a gene that produces a chemical that glows in blue light. A mouse doesn't normally have this chemical. This glowing mouse has been genetically modified.

Genes can be transferred from any kind of organism to any other kind of organism, e.g. bacteria, humans, other animals, plants.

| the gene for a characteristic is 'cut out' of a chromosome using enzymes | → | the gene is inserted into a chromosome inside the nucleus of a cell in a different organism | → | the cell of this organism now produces the characteristic from the gene |

Worked example   target D-C

Read the following information about genetically modified mice.

- If the gene is inserted into an early-stage mouse embryo, all the mouse cells will contain the gene, and the gene can be passed on to offspring.
- Mice can be genetically modified so they suffer from human-like diseases, such as cancer.
- New treatments for human cancer can be developed more quickly using GM mice.
- GM mice would not survive long in the wild.

Use only this information in your answer. Give **one** reason why some people are in favour of genetic modification of mice and **one** reason why some people are against it.   *(2 marks)*

For: Using GM mice means that new cancer treatments develop more quickly, which could help people.

Against: The GM mice will suffer diseases that they wouldn't normally get.

Other answers are possible as long as you only use information from the question.

EXAM ALERT!

Remember that adult cell cloning and genetic engineering are two different processes. Adult cell cloning involves transferring a nucleus but genetic engineering means transferring a gene.

Students have struggled with questions like this in recent exams – **be prepared!**

GM crops

GM CROP plants have been genetically modified to give them new characteristics, such as:

- resistance to attack by insects
- resistance to HERBICIDES, so that fields can be sprayed to kill weeds, but not the crop.

These characteristics can help the crop grow better and produce more food (an increased YIELD).

Now try this

target G-E

1 What is meant by genetic engineering?   *(2 marks)*

target D-C

2 Describe how a GM crop with herbicide resistance could be developed.   *(2 marks)*

Issues with new science

New scientific developments cause new issues that we need to think about. To make good judgements about these developments we need good information.

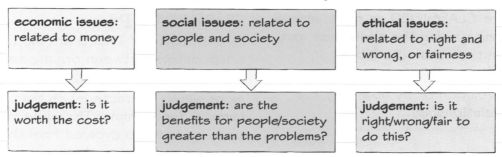

economic issues: related to money	social issues: related to people and society	ethical issues: related to right and wrong, or fairness
judgement: is it worth the cost?	judgement: are the benefits for people/society greater than the problems?	judgement: is it right/wrong/fair to do this?

If you are asked a question on genetic engineering or adult cell cloning, the example used may not be something you have studied in class. Don't panic. All the information you need to answer the question will be on the paper. If you are asked to make an informed judgement you could think about the different kinds of issues shown on the flow chart.

Concerns about GM crops

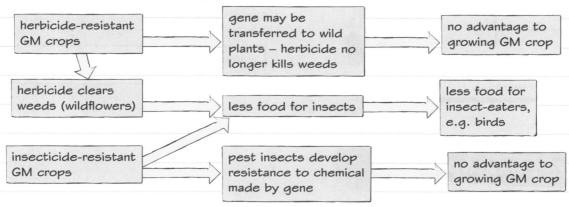

herbicide-resistant GM crops → gene may be transferred to wild plants – herbicide no longer kills weeds → no advantage to growing GM crop

herbicide clears weeds (wildflowers) → less food for insects → less food for insect-eaters, e.g. birds

insecticide-resistant GM crops → pest insects develop resistance to chemical made by gene → no advantage to growing GM crop

Worked example G-E

Foods made from GM crops have been sold in the US for over 10 years. Scientific studies show no evidence that GM foods harm health. Suggest why some people are still concerned about the possible effects on health of eating GM foods. *(2 marks)*

There is a possibility that eating these foods over a long time may harm health. These effects would not show yet because GM foods have only been available for a few years.

Now try this

1 Give one concern about the effect of insect-resistant GM crops on the environment. *(1 mark)*

2 If the gene for herbicide resistance is transferred to weed plants, there will be no advantage in growing the GM crop. Describe the economic impact of this. *(2 marks)*

Evolution

EVOLUTION means change over time.

Classification

Organisms are CLASSIFIED as plant, animal or microorganism using the similarities and differences in their characteristics.

Classification can show how organisms are related by evolution or by how they live (ecological relationship).

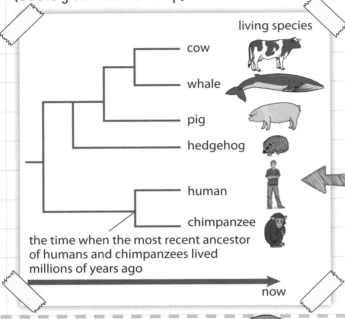

living species

cow

whale

pig

hedgehog

human

chimpanzee

the time when the most recent ancestor of humans and chimpanzees lived millions of years ago

now

Models of evolutionary relationships

EVOLUTIONARY TREES are models of the relationships between organisms.

This tree shows that cows and whales have more similar characteristics than cows and humans, for example. This suggests that cows and whales evolved from the same ancestor more recently than cows and humans.

EXAM ALERT!

Different kinds of evolutionary tree are based on different evidence and so may look different. You need to understand what an evolutionary tree shows, so that you can interpret it, no matter what it looks like.

Students have struggled with this topic in recent exams – **be prepared!**

Worked example   target D-C

The diagram shows the forelimbs of two mammals. Suggest how this evidence supports the idea that these mammals evolved from the same ancestor.   *(2 marks)*

The bones in each limb are arranged in the same way. This suggests they evolved from the same ancestor with this bone arrangement.

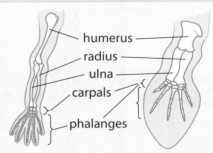

humerus
radius
ulna
carpals
phalanges

human arm – for holding and working with objects

whale flipper – for swimming underwater

Now try this

target G-E

1 Describe how organisms are classified.   *(2 marks)*

target D-C

2 Look at the evolutionary tree above.

(a) What does the tree show about how similar humans, cows and pigs are?   *(2 marks)*

(b) Which of these pairs of animals shares the most recent common ancestor: cow/pig, cow/hedgehog? Explain your answer.   *(2 marks)*

Theories of evolution

There are two important theories of how evolution happens.

 ## Darwin's theory

Darwin's theory states that evolution happens through NATURAL SELECTION.

Natural selection works on inherited characteristics (caused by GENES).

Relatively rapid evolution can occur if:

- a new form of a gene occurs due to MUTATION
- there is a large change in the environment.

| individuals in a species vary in their characteristics – some of these variations are caused by genes | → | some variations are better suited to the environment than others | → | individuals with the better-suited variations are more likely to breed successfully and pass on genes for the better-suited variations | → | the next generation will contain more individuals with the genes for better-suited variations |

 ## Lamarck's theory

Long before Darwin, Lamarck thought evolution was due to the inheritance of characteristics changed by the environment.

> Darwin's theory explains evolution better than Lamarck's theory in most cases.
> You need to learn the differences between Darwin's and Lamarck's theories.

| environmental factor, e.g. weight training | → | causes an **acquired characteristic** e.g. increased muscle size | → | acquired characteristic inherited by offspring, e.g. children have big muscles |

Worked example G-E

SPEC AQA SKILL

Give one reason why Darwin's theory was only gradually accepted. *(2 marks)*

At the time that Darwin published his theory, many people believed God had created all the species. So they didn't believe evolution could happen just by natural selection.

Other possible answers are:

- Darwin's theory was published about 50 years before the theory about genes, so he couldn't explain how variations were passed on to offspring.
- Evolution happens slowly, so it can take a long time to collect evidence that evolution has happened.

Now try this

 D-C

1 Jack practised hard to become a champion swimmer. Years later, his daughter trained hard and also became a champion swimmer.

  (a) Suggest how Lamarck would have explained the evolution of being a champion swimmer. *(2 marks)*

  (b) Suggest how Darwin would have explained this. *(2 marks)*

  (c) Explain why we now know that Darwin's theory is a better explanation of how evolution occurs. *(2 marks)*

Biology six mark question 3

There will be one 6 mark question on your exam paper which will be marked for *Quality of Written Communication as well as scientific knowledge*. This means that you need to apply your scientific knowledge, present your answer in a logical and organised way and make sure that your spelling, grammar and punctuation are as good as you can make them.

Worked example

In parts of Africa the maize crops are badly damaged each year by pests. This leaves little food for the farmers and their families to eat.

A new variety of genetically modified maize has been produced using a gene from a bacterium, and this new variety is resistant to the pests. The seed for the GM maize is more expensive than seed for normal maize, but it guarantees a good yield.

Describe how the GM maize was produced and explain some of the arguments for and against GM crops. *(6 marks)*

The gene for resistance to the pests was taken out of the bacterium. The gene was inserted into the maize plants to make them resistant to the pests.

Arguments for growing GM maize are that the maize plants will produce a greater yield, which means that the farmers and their families will have more food to eat.

Arguments against growing the GM maize are that it is more expensive than growing normal maize, and some people think that GM food could be harmful to health.

EXAM ALERT!

Remember that these questions take into account how good your punctuation is. Make sure that you start each sentence with a capital letter and end with a full stop.

Students have struggled with questions like this in recent exams – **be prepared!**

This answer gives two different points about how a GM plant could be made, but it really should explain that the gene was put into a very early stage of a maize plant, so that all the cells of the adult plant contained the gene.

This question doesn't tell you to use only what's written to help you write your answer. So you could give other arguments for and against that you remember from your course, such as people are worried that GM crops harm the wildflowers and insects other than the pests, or that pests are evolving so they can grow on these resistant crops.

Now try this

1 Describe the roles of different organisms in the carbon cycle.

decomposers   primary consumer   secondary consumer   producer   *(6 marks)*

Atoms and elements

Elements

All substances are made of ATOMS. An individual atom is too small for you to see, so everything around you contains very many atoms.

An ELEMENT is a substance that is made of only one sort of atom. Oxygen is an element because it only contains oxygen atoms.

Chemical symbols

There are about 100 different elements. Atoms of each element are given a chemical symbol.

Every symbol starts with a capital letter, usually followed by a lower case letter.

For example, N represents a nitrogen atom, but Na represents a sodium atom.

The elements are shown in the PERIODIC TABLE.

Periodic table

1   2 ←——————— group numbers ——————→ 3   4   5   6   7   0

					1 H Hydrogen 1			Non-metals on the right									4 He Helium 2
7 Li Lithium 7	9 Be Beryllium 4	Each group (a vertical column) contains elements with similar properties									11 B Boron 5	12 C Carbon 6	14 N Nitrogen 7	16 O Oxygen 8	19 F Fluorine 9	20 Ne Neon 10
23 Na Sodium 11	24 Mg Magnesium 12			Metals on the left							27 Al Aluminium 13	28 Si Silicon 14	31 P Phosphorous 15	32 S Sulfur 16	35.5 Cl Chlorine 17	40 Ar Argon 18
39 K Potassium 19	40 Ca Calcium 20	45 Sc Scandium 21	48 Ti Titanium 22	51 V Vanadium 23	52 Cr Chromium 24	55 Mn Manganese 25	56 Fe Iron 26	59 Co Cobalt 27	59 Ni Nickel 28	64 Cu Copper 29	65 Zn Zinc 30	70 Ga Gallium 31	73 Ge Germanium 32	75 As Arsenic 33	79 Se Selenium 34	80 Br Bromine 35	84 Kr Krypton 36
85 Rb Rubidium 37	88 Sr Strontium 38	89 Y Yttrium 39	91 Zr Zirconium 40	93 Nb Niobium 41	96 Mo Molybdenum 42	99 Tc Technetium 43	101 Ru Ruthenium 44	103 Rh Rhodium 45	106 Pd Palladium 46	108 Ag Silver 47	112 Cd Cadmium 48	115 In Indium 49	119 Sn Tin 50	122 Sb Antimony 51	128 Te Tellurium 52	127 I Iodine 53	131 Xe Xenon 54
133 Cs Caesium 55	137 Ba Barium 56	139 La Lanthanum 4	178 Hf Hafnium 72	181 Ta Tantalum 73	184 W Tungsten 74	186 Re Rhenium 75	190 Os Osmium 76	192 Ir Iridium 77	195 Pt Platinum 78	197 Au Gold 79	201 Hg Mercury 80	204 Tl Thallium 81	207 Pb Lead 82	209 Bi Bismuth 83	[209] Po Polonium 84	[210] At Astatine 85	[222] Rn Radon 86
223 Fr Francium 87	226 Ra Radium 88	227 Ac Actinium 89	261 Rf Rutherfordium 104	262 Db Dubnium 105	266 Sg Seaborgium 106	264 Bh Bohrium 107	277 Hs Hassium 108	268 Mt Meitnerium 109	271 Ds Darmstadtium 110	272 Rg Roentgenium 111	Elements with atomic numbers 112 – 116 have been reported but not fully authenticated						

Worked example

target G-E

Complete the table to show the name and relative electrical charge of each type of particle in an atom. *(2 marks)*

Name of particle	Relative charge
proton	+1
neutron	0
electron	−1

EXAM ALERT!

Remember neutrons are **neutral** – not negative.

Students have struggled with questions like this in recent exams – **be prepared!**

Atoms have a small central **nucleus** made of positively charged **protons** and neutral **neutrons**.

There are negatively charged **electrons** around the nucleus.

Now try this

target G-E

1. Draw a ring around the correct answer to complete each sentence.

   (a) The centre of each atom is called the | neutron   nucleus   molecule | *(1 mark)*

   (b) Around the centre of each atom there are | electrons   protons   bonds | *(1 mark)*

2. Sodium and oxygen are both elements. Sodium is a metal.

target D-C

   (a) Explain why sodium is called an element.   *(1 mark)*

   (b) Why does oxygen have different properties than sodium?   *(1 mark)*

Particles in atoms

Protons, neutrons and electrons are called SUBATOMIC PARTICLES. You can work out how many of each type of subatomic particle an atom has from its atomic number and mass number.

Atomic number

The number of protons in an atom of an element is called its ATOMIC NUMBER.

The atoms of different elements have different numbers of protons – no two elements can have the same atomic number.

Number of electrons

Atoms have no overall charge. This is because the number of electrons in an atom is the same as the number of protons.

Mass number

The total number of protons and neutrons in an atom is called its MASS NUMBER.

Worked example   target D-C

A sodium atom has an atomic number of 11 and a mass number of 23. How many of each type of subatomic particle does it have?

(3 marks)

Number of protons = 11

Number of electrons = 11

Number of neutrons = 12

The number of protons is given by the atomic number, which is 11 for sodium.

The number of electrons in an atom is the same as the number of protons, which is 11 here.

The number of neutrons equals the mass number minus the atomic number.

So the number of neutrons = 23 − 11 = 12.

Diagrams of atoms

Atoms of elements can be drawn like the one in this diagram. This means that it is easy to work out how many subatomic particles there are.

In this particular diagram, the crosses represent electrons. They are arranged around the central nucleus.

If the atom has three electrons, it must also have three protons. This means that the black circles represent protons here.

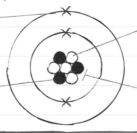

The white circles here represent neutrons.

The atomic number is 3 and the mass number is 7 (3 protons + 4 neutrons).

1 An atom has an atomic number of 4 and a mass number of 9. How many protons does it have?

(1 mark)

2 The diagrams on the right represent two atoms, A and B.

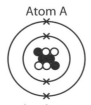
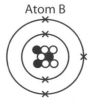

Atom A   Atom B

(a) In these diagrams, which symbol represents the following particles. Choose from: ● ○ ×.
(i) a proton   **(ii)** a neutron   **(iii)** an electron?   *(3 marks)*

(b) What is the mass number of atom B?   *(1 mark)*

Electronic structure

You should be able to represent the electronic structure of the first 20 elements.

Energy levels

The electrons in an atom occupy different ENERGY LEVELS around the nucleus. Each electron in an atom is at a particular energy level. Electrons occupy the lowest available energy levels.

Shells

Energy levels are also called SHELLS:
- The innermost shell is the lowest energy level.
- The outer shell is the highest occupied energy level.

Writing electronic structures

Different energy levels can contain different maximum numbers of electrons. For the first 20 elements (hydrogen to calcium):

Energy level	Number of electrons
first	1 or 2
second	up to 8
third	up to 8
fourth	1 or 2

For example, a sodium atom has 11 electrons:
- 2 fit into the first energy level
- 8 fit into the second energy level
- 1 fits into the third energy level.

This electronic structure is written as 2,8,1 (the commas separate each energy level).

Use your periodic table to work out electronic structures. Count from hydrogen to the required element, for example sodium.

Electronic structures as diagrams

This is the electronic structure of sodium as a diagram.

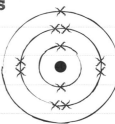

(a) Write the electronic structure of oxygen.

(b) Complete the diagram to show the electronic structure of oxygen (atomic number 8).   *(2 marks)*

(a) 2,6   (b)

Make sure you can write and draw electronic structures correctly. The periodic table on the Data Sheet can help you:
- The number of energy levels (or circles) must be the same as the row the element is in.
- The total number of electrons must be the same as the element's atomic number.
- The last number must be the same as the element's group number.

Students have struggled with questions like this in recent exams – **be prepared!**

---

1 Write the electronic structures for atoms of the following elements:
  (a) carbon (atomic number 6)   *(1 mark)*
  (b) sulfur (atomic number 16)   *(1 mark)*
  (c) calcium (atomic number 20).   *(1 mark)*

2 Complete the diagram to show the electronic structure of aluminium (atomic number 13).   *(2 marks)*

Electronic structure and groups

Atoms of the elements in a group in the periodic table have the same number of electrons in their highest energy level (outer shell). This gives the elements similar chemical properties.

Group 1

The elements in Group 1 include lithium, sodium and potassium. Their atoms all have just one electron in their highest occupied energy level (outer shell).

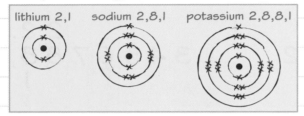

lithium 2,1   sodium 2,8,1   potassium 2,8,8,1

Reaction of Group 1 elements with oxygen

These elements burn vigorously in oxygen to produce solid metal oxides.

Reaction of Group 1 elements with water

These elements react vigorously with water to produce hydrogen gas and metal hydroxides that dissolve to form alkaline solutions.

Group 0

The elements in Group 0 include helium, neon and argon. The highest occupied energy levels (outer shells) of their atoms are full:
* Helium has two electrons in its highest occupied energy level.
* The others all have eight electrons in their highest occupied energy levels.

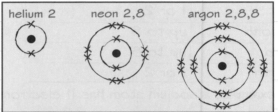

helium 2   neon 2,8   argon 2,8,8

Worked example   target D-C

Explain the chemical properties of the Group 0 elements.   *(2 marks)*

The Group 0 elements are all unreactive. This is because their atoms have stable arrangements of electrons.

The answer states the main chemical property of the Group 0 elements, and states why they have this property. Their stable arrangements are due to their full highest energy levels.

Common names

Group 1 elements are called the ALKALI METALS because they react with water to form alkalis. Group 0 elements are called the NOBLE GASES because they are unreactive.

Now try this

target G-E

1 Sodium is in Group 1. How many electrons are there in the highest occupied energy levels of its atoms?   *(1 mark)*

target D-C

2 Why do the elements in Group 1 have similar chemical properties?   *(1 mark)*

3 How many electrons in there in the outer energy levels of the elements in Group 0?   *(2 marks)*

Making compounds

When elements react with each other, their atoms join together to form COMPOUNDS.

Forming ions

Metals and non-metals react together to form compounds. The compounds are made of IONS.

An ion is a charged particle formed when an atom, or group of atoms, loses or gains electrons.

Forming molecules

Compounds formed from reactions between non-metals consist of MOLECULES.

In a molecule, electrons are shared between atoms. These shared electrons make COVALENT BONDS, which hold the atoms in the molecule together.

Giving and taking electrons

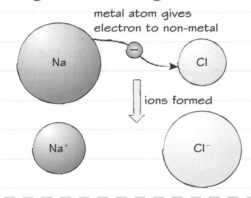

metal atom gives electron to non-metal

ions formed

Some example molecules

Carbon dioxide, CO_2 (a compound of carbon and oxygen)

Water, H_2O (a compound of hydrogen and oxygen)

Worked example   *target* **G-E**

Potassium and bromine react together to form potassium bromide.

(a) Explain how potassium atoms form ions.
(2 marks)

(b) Explain how bromine atoms form ions.
(2 marks)

(a) Potassium atoms lose electrons. This means they form positive ions.

(b) Bromine atoms gain electrons. This means they form negative ions.

Potassium is a metal and bromine is a non-metal. When they react together, potassium atoms give electrons to bromine atoms, forming ions.

Remember:
- metals lose electrons to form positive ions
- non-metals gain electrons to form negative ions.

The oppositely charged ions attract each other in compounds containing ions.

Remember that metals are on the left of the periodic table, and non-metals are on the right.

Now try this

target **G-E**

1 Tick (✓) **two** correct statements about compounds. *(2 marks)*

Statement	Tick (✓)
Compounds formed from metals consist of molecules	
Covalent bonds hold metals together in molecules	
Compounds formed from metals and non-metals consist of ions	
Non-metals gain electrons to form negative ions	

target **D-C**

2 State the type of bond found in sulfur dioxide.
(1 mark)

Chemical equations

We use word equations and balanced symbol equations to represent chemical reactions.

Word equations

In a chemical reaction:

- REACTANTS are the substances that react together
- PRODUCTS are the substances made.

In a WORD EQUATION, two or more reactants or products are separated by a + sign.

An example word equation

This word equation shows that iron oxide reacts with carbon to make iron and carbon monoxide:

iron oxide + carbon → iron + carbon monoxide
(reactants)   (products)

Take care to show all the reactants on the left of the arrow and all the products on the right.

Symbol equations

In a SYMBOL EQUATION, the chemical FORMULA of each reactant and product is shown, instead of its name.

In a correctly balanced symbol equation, there are the same number of atoms of each element in the reactants and in the products.

Here is the symbol equation for the reaction between iron oxide and carbon:

$$Fe_2O_3 + 3C \rightarrow 2Fe + 3CO$$

The symbol equation shows that each side has 2 Fe atoms, 3 O atoms, and 3 C atoms.

Worked example G-E

Carbon reacts with oxygen to make carbon dioxide:

carbon + oxygen → carbon dioxide

Calculate the mass of carbon dioxide formed by the reaction of 3 g of carbon with 8 g of oxygen. *(1 mark)*

mass = 3 g + 8 g = 11 g

In chemical reactions, no atoms are lost and no new atoms are made.

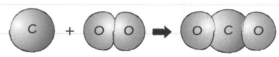

This means that the total mass of the products is the same as the total mass of the reactants.

Now try this

 1 Calcium carbonate breaks down when heated:

calcium carbonate → calcium oxide + carbon dioxide
    50 g   ?   22 g

Calculate the mass of calcium oxide made from 50 g of calcium carbonate. *(1 mark)*

 2 (a) Describe, in as much detail as you can, what this word equation shows:

lead nitrate + potassium iodide → lead iodide + potassium nitrate *(2 marks)*

(b) Draw a ring around the correct answer to complete the sentence. *(1 mark)*

When lead nitrate reacts with potassium iodide, the total mass

| goes up | stays the same | goes down |

3 Explain, in terms of the number of atoms, why this is a correct symbol equation. *(2 marks)*

$$H_2 + F_2 \rightarrow 2HF$$

Limestone

LIMESTONE is a type of rock. It is mostly calcium carbonate, $CaCO_3$. Limestone is used as a building material.

Uses of limestone

As raw material for making cement, mortar and concrete.

As blocks and slabs for walls and pavements.

As AGGREGATE (small lumps) for the base of roads and railways.

Building materials from limestone

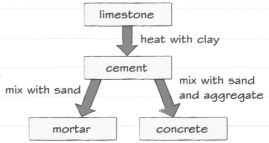

limestone

↓ heat with clay

cement

mix with sand ↙   ↘ mix with sand and aggregate

mortar   concrete

The dry ingredients for mortar or concrete are mixed with water. The mixtures then set hard.

Quarries

Limestone is taken from the ground in QUARRIES. Obtaining and using limestone has economic and social effects. For example:

✓ New jobs are created and limestone is a valuable material for building.

✗ Fewer tourists may visit an area that has a working quarry.

Limestone, cement and concrete are needed for buildings. Their positive effects must be considered against the negative effects of a quarry.

Limestone quarrying has impacts that cause environmental problems. Tick (✓) **two** impacts that cause environmental problems.   *(2 marks)*

Impact of quarrying	Tick ✓
Extra traffic	✓
More jobs	
Noise pollution	✓
Tourists put off	

Extra traffic comes from the lorries needed to transport the limestone from the quarry to the customers. Roads may need to be widened or new ones built.

Lorries release carbon dioxide from their burning diesel fuel. Carbon dioxide is a **greenhouse gas**.

Noise pollution comes from machinery and vehicles, and from blasting rock.

1 Describe two ways in which a limestone quarry may benefit local people.   *(2 marks)*

2 Building blocks for walls may be made from limestone, or from concrete poured into moulds. Choose the material you think is better for making walls; limestone or concrete. Describe two advantages your choice has compared with the other material.   *(2 marks)*

Calcium carbonate chemistry

Thermal decomposition

Many metal carbonates break down when they are heated. The reaction is called THERMAL DECOMPOSITION.

metal carbonate	→	metal oxide	+	carbon dioxide

When calcium carbonate is heated, it decomposes to form calcium oxide and carbon dioxide.

Other carbonates

These carbonates decompose in a similar way to calcium carbonate when heated:
- magnesium carbonate
- zinc carbonate
- copper carbonate.

Not all carbonates of metals in Group 1 decompose when heated with a Bunsen flame.

Making an alkali

Calcium oxide reacts vigorously with drops of water to make a white solid called calcium hydroxide. A lot of heat is given out in the reaction. Calcium hydroxide is an ALKALI.

Alkalis dissolve in water to make **alkaline** solutions. They **neutralise** acids.

Limewater

LIMEWATER is a solution of calcium hydroxide in water. It is used as a test for carbon dioxide. Carbon dioxide turns limewater cloudy (because tiny white particles of calcium carbonate form in the reaction):

calcium hydroxide + carbon dioxide → calcium carbonate + water

Worked example   target G-E

A statue is made from limestone. It has been damaged by acid rain. Complete the word equation to show the reaction.   *(2 marks)*

calcium carbonate + sulfuric acid

↓

calcium sulfate
+ <u>carbon dioxide</u> + <u>water</u>

Excess acid in lakes and soil can be neutralised by adding powdered limestone, which is mainly calcium carbonate.

Other carbonates react with acids, including:
- sodium carbonate
- magnesium carbonate
- zinc carbonate
- copper carbonate.

Any acid reacts with a carbonate to produce a salt, carbon dioxide and water.

Now try this

 target G-E
1 Draw a ring around the correct substance to complete the sentence.   *(1 mark)*

Copper carbonate breaks down when heated to produce a gas and

copper chloride	copper oxide
copper hydroxide	

 target G-E
2 (a) Describe how limewater is used as a test for carbon dioxide.   *(1 mark)*

(b) Name the solid produced in this test.   *(1 mark)*

 target D-C
3 Write a word equation for the reaction between calcium oxide and water.   *(1 mark)*

4 Explain why bubbles are seen when sodium carbonate is mixed with an acid.   *(2 marks)*

Chemistry six mark question 1

There will be one 6 mark question on your exam paper which will be marked for *Quality of Written Communication as well as scientific knowledge.* This means that you need to apply your scientific knowledge, present your answer in a logical and organised way and make sure that your spelling, grammar and punctuation are as good as you can make them.

Worked example

Limestone is important for building but to extract it from the Earth it must be quarried. Explosives and heavy machinery are used to get the limestone out of the ground and move it. Large lorries take the crushed limestone to the cement factory. The machinery and lorries use diesel fuel.

A quarry company wants to open a new limestone quarry in an attractive countryside area. Describe the positive and negative impacts of quarrying limestone there. *(6 marks)*

A limestone quarry will create new jobs in the area. This will improve the local economy and may attract other new businesses into the area. Limestone is a useful building material, and cement can be used to make mortar and concrete. These are valuable materials.

However, a limestone quarry will damage the environment. It will be noisy and look unpleasant. The habitats of local wildlife will be destroyed. The machinery and lorries will release smoke and carbon dioxide.

A balanced answer

The information given will help you with your answer but you should not just repeat it.

It is important to give detailed descriptions of some advantages *and* disadvantages of the quarry.

 The answer could also have mentioned how the company might restore the land after the quarry closes, or improve local facilities such as roads.

 The use of 'however' is a good way moving to the disadvantages. Note that it gives specific examples of the damage to the environment.

Now try this

Limestone and brick are often used for constructing the outside walls of buildings. Use the information in the table, and what you know about limestone and brick, to explain the advantages and disadvantages of using limestone as a building material. *(6 marks)*

Building material	Cost (£ per m²)	Energy needed to extract and process material (MJ/kg)	Resistance to air pollution	Life span (years)
Limestone	52	0.85	Medium	50 or more
Brick	39	3.00	High	50 or more

45

Extracting metals

Unreactive metals such as gold are found in the Earth's crust as the metal element itself. However, most metals are found as compounds. These need chemical reactions to extract them from their ores.

Ores

Rocks contain metals or their compounds. An ORE is a rock that contains enough of a metal to make its extraction economical.

Rocks may contain too little metal to make extraction worthwhile (if the cost of extracting the metal is greater than the value of the metal itself). Over time, metal prices may rise and these LOW-GRADE ORES may become useful.

Reduction

Iron is extracted from iron oxide in a blast furnace by reaction with carbon:

iron oxide + carbon → iron + carbon dioxide

This reaction works because carbon is more reactive than iron.

Other metals can be extracted like this if they are less reactive than carbon.

A reaction where oxygen is removed from a compound is called a REDUCTION reaction.

Worked example G-E

Aluminium must be extracted from its oxide by electrolysis.

(a) Why is reduction with carbon not used?
Tick (✓) the correct answer. *(1 mark)*

Answer	Tick (✓)
carbon is more reactive than aluminium	
aluminium is more reactive than carbon	✓
carbon is less reactive than oxygen	

(b) Suggest why aluminium extraction is expensive. *(1 mark)*

Large amounts of electrical energy are needed for electrolysis.

Titanium cannot be extracted by reduction with carbon, either. As with aluminium, a lot of energy and many stages are needed.

Reactivity and extraction

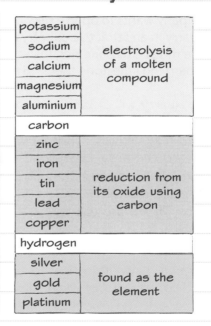

potassium	
sodium	
calcium	electrolysis of a molten compound
magnesium	
aluminium	
carbon	
zinc	
iron	
tin	reduction from its oxide using carbon
lead	
copper	
hydrogen	
silver	
gold	found as the element
platinum	

most reactive (most difficult and expensive to extract)

least reactive (easiest and cheapest to extract)

Now try this

 G-E

1 Copper can be extracted by heating copper oxide with carbon. Write the word equation for the reaction. *(2 marks)*

2 (a) What is an ore? *(2 marks)*

(b) Lead can be obtained by removing oxygen from lead oxide. What is this reaction called? *(1 mark)*

 D-C

3 Predict the method used to extract potassium. Explain your answer. *(2 marks)*

Extracting copper

High-grade copper ores contain a high proportion of copper compounds.

Smelting

Copper is extracted from these ores by SMELTING. This involves heating the copper ores in a furnace. For example, copper sulfide is heated in air to produce copper:

copper sulfide + oxygen → copper + sulfur dioxide

Traditional mining and extraction methods have major environmental impacts. High-grade ores are running out, so other extraction methods are being researched.

Electrolysis

Copper is purified by ELECTROLYSIS.

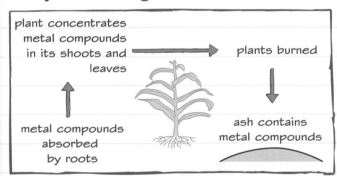

positive electrode   negative electrode

Impure copper — positive copper ions → pure copper

impurities form a sludge

copper(II) sulfate solution

Scrap iron can be used to produce copper from solutions of copper salts. Draw a ring around the correct answer to complete each sentence.

(2 marks)

(a) Iron is
- (more reactive than copper.)
- more expensive than copper.
- less abundant than copper.

(b) The type of reaction is
- neutralisation.
- electrolysis.
- (displacement.)

Iron is more reactive than copper. This means it can **displace** copper from solutions of copper compounds. For example:

iron + copper sulfate → iron sulfate + copper

Scrap iron is cheap and abundant, so copper can be extracted cheaply this way.

Phytomining

plant concentrates metal compounds in its shoots and leaves → plants burned

metal compounds absorbed by roots

ash contains metal compounds

Bioleaching

Copper can also be extracted by BIOLEACHING. Certain bacteria absorb metal compounds to produce a solution called LEACHATE. This has a high concentration of metal compounds. Scrap iron may be used to displace copper metal from these solutions.

G-E

1 Tick (✓) **two** correct statements about phytomining and bioleaching.   *(2 marks)*

Statement	Tick (✓)
phytomining uses plants to absorb metal compounds	
a leachate is an ash containing metal compounds	
bioleaching is used with copper-rich ores	
phytomining uses less energy than traditional mining	

D-C   **2** Explain why supplies of copper may be limited in the future.   *(2 marks)*

Recycling metals

Recycling metals instead of extracting them from ores has many benefits.

Extracting metals

Extracting metals from their ores:

- ✗ uses up limited resources
- ✗ uses a lot of energy
- ✗ damages the environment.

Recycling metals reduces these disadvantages. Used metal items are collected. Rather than throwing them away, these are taken apart. The metal is melted down to make new items.

Recycling

- ✓ metal ores will last longer
- ✓ less energy needed to recycle metals than to mine ores and exract metals
- ✓ fewer quarries and mines needed
- ✓ less noise and dust produced
- ✓ less land needed for landfill sites.

Worked example

D–C

SPEC AQA SKILL

The flow chart shows the main stages in extracting aluminium from its ore.

Use it to suggest the benefits of recycling aluminium. *(3 marks)*

Less waste rock will be produced from mining. Aluminium oxide will not need separating and purifying from aluminium ore, which will save energy. Less carbon dioxide will be emitted because less fuel will be needed for heat and electricity and because carbon dioxide is produced from the electrolysis.

You need to be specific in your answer. To write that recycling is 'better for the environment' does not give enough detail.

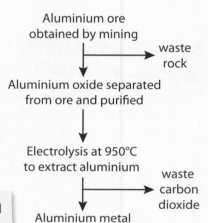

Aluminium ore obtained by mining → waste rock

Aluminium oxide separated from ore and purified

Electrolysis at 950°C to extract aluminium → waste carbon dioxide

Aluminium metal

Recycling metals saves energy

A recent study reported these findings.

metal	% energy saving
aluminium	94
iron and steel	70
copper	86

Drawbacks of recycling

- ✗ Used metal items must be collected and transported to the recycling centre.
- ✗ Different metals must be removed from used items and sorted.
- ✗ Recycling saves different amounts of energy, depending on the metal involved.

Now try this

G–E

1 Less fossil fuel is used when steel is recycled instead of extracting it from iron ore. Tick (✓) one advantage and tick (✓) one disadvantage of recycling steel. *(2 marks)*

Statement	Advantage tick (✓)	Disadvantage tick (✓)
more iron ore needs to be mined		
used steel items must be collected and transported		
less carbon dioxide is produced		
iron is the second most common metal in the Earth's crust		

D–C   **2** Describe two ways in which recycling copper can reduce pollution. *(2 marks)*

Steel and other alloys

Most metals in everyday use are mixtures of metals called ALLOYS.

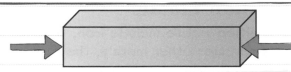

Cast iron

Iron oxide is reduced to iron in a BLAST FURNACE. Iron straight from the blast furnace is about 96% pure. The impurities it contains make the iron BRITTLE and this limits its uses.

Blast furnace iron is used as CAST IRON.

Cast iron is strong in compression.

Cast iron has been used to make manhole covers, drain pipes and pillars in buildings. It is now used to make pans and garden furniture.

Steels

Most iron is converted into STEEL. There are different types of steel, but they are all alloys. Steels are mixtures of iron and carbon, often with other metals.

Low-carbon steel is easily shaped.

High-carbon steel is hard.

Stainless steel is resistant to corrosion.

Worked example

 target D–C

The table shows some typical properties of gold alloys.

Gold alloy	% copper	Relative strength	Relative hardness
18 carat	20.5	4.1	4.4
22 carat	5.1	2.6	2.3
24 carat	0	1	1

(a) Use information from the table to explain why copper is mixed with gold. *(2 marks)*

(b) Suggest another reason why gold is alloyed with copper. *(1 mark)*

(a) To make the gold stronger and harder.
(b) Copper is cheaper than gold.

Notice that the gold alloys become stronger and harder the more copper they contain.

Pure gold, copper, iron and aluminium are too soft for many uses. For everyday use, they are mixed with small amounts of similar metals to make them harder. For example, copper is mixed with zinc to make brass.

EXAM ALERT!

Take care to use information given in the question, rather than just repeating it.

Students have struggled with questions like this in recent exams – **be prepared!**

Now try this

 target G–E

1 Stainless steels contain chromium. Draw a ring around the correct answer to complete the sentence. *(1 mark)*
The chromium in stainless steels make the metal | easily shaped.
hard.
resistant to corrosion.

2 What is an alloy? *(1 mark)*

 target D–C

3 Explain why iron from the blast furnace has limited uses. *(2 marks)*

Transition metals

The elements in the central block of the periodic table are called the TRANSITION METALS.

Transition metals

The transition metals include iron, titanium and copper. Like other metals, they:

- are good conductors of heat
- are good conductors of electricity
- can be bent or hammered into shape.

These properties make them useful:

- as structural materials
- for making things that need to let heat or electricity pass through them easily.

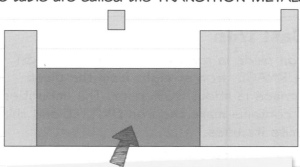

The transition metals are between groups 2 and 3 in the periodic table.

Worked example

target **G-E**

SPEC AQA SKILL

Copper has useful properties. These make it suitable for electrical wiring and plumbing.

Draw a line from each use to the correct property.

(2 marks)

Use	Property
	good heat conductor
electrical wiring	good electrical conductor
water pipes	does not react with water

Copper is also a good conductor of heat, but this is not the relevant property for making electrical wiring and water pipes. This property would make copper useful for making pans or cooling fins for computer chips, for example.

Copper can be bent but is hard enough for pipes or tanks.

Aluminium and titanium

SPEC AQA SKILL

Aluminium and titanium have these properties in common:

- low density (lightweight for their size)
- resistant to corrosion.

Titanium is used for artificial hip joints.

Aluminium is used for aircraft parts.

Now try this

target **G-E**

1 Copper and iron are transition metals. Name one other transition metal. *(1 mark)*

2 Steel and aluminium may be used to make car body panels.

	Steel	Aluminium
Relative strength	1.0	0.4
Effect of damp air	corrodes quickly	does not corrode
Density in g/cm³	7.9	2.7

(a) State one disadvantage of using aluminium to make car body panels. *(1 mark)*

(b) State one advantage of using aluminium to make car body panels. *(1 mark)*

target **D-C**

3 Artificial hip joints may be made from stainless steel or titanium. Use your knowledge and understanding to explain which metal is better for making hip joints. *(3 marks)*

Hydrocarbons

Crude oil is a mixture of a very large number of compounds, most of which are hydrocarbons.

Alkanes

A HYDROCARBON is a compound made up of hydrogen atoms and carbon atoms ONLY. Most of the hydrocarbon molecules in crude oil are ALKANES.

Alkanes have the general formula C_nH_{2n+2}. For example, the chemical formula for butane (which contains four carbon atoms) is C_4H_{10}.

> The atoms in hydrocarbon molecules are joined together by **covalent bonds**.

EXAM ALERT!

Take care when writing the formulae for alkanes: C^4H^{10} or C4H10 would be wrong.

Students have struggled with this topic in recent exams – **be prepared!**

Formulae of alkanes

An alkane molecule can be represented by its CHEMICAL FORMULA or by its DISPLAYED STRUCTURE.

methane, CH_4

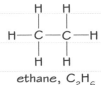

ethane, C_2H_6

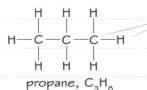

propane, C_3H_8

Each hydrogen atom has one bond and each carbon atom has four bonds.

The names of alkanes end in 'ane'.

Worked example *target* G-E

Butane can be represented as:

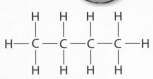

Use the correct words from the box to complete the sentences. *(2 marks)*

| bond saturated element compound |

(a) Butane is a <u>saturated</u> hydrocarbon.
(b) Each line in the formula represents a covalent <u>bond</u>.

> The diagram shows the displayed structure of butane. Its chemical formula is C_4H_{10}. Each line in the displayed structure represents a covalent bond. Remember that covalent bonds form when atoms share electrons.

> You need to know the names of the four alkanes on this page.

> Alkanes are saturated hydrocarbons – their carbon atoms are joined together by single covalent bonds only.

Now try this

1 Each octane molecule has 8 carbon atoms and 18 hydrogen atoms. Write the chemical formula for octane.

(1 mark)

target D-C

2 Crude oil contains saturated hydrocarbons. State what is meant by:
(a) saturated *(1 mark)*
(b) hydrocarbon. *(1 mark)*

3 Compound X has the formula C_5H_{12}. Explain why X is an alkane. *(2 marks)*

Crude oil and alkanes

Mixtures

The substances in a mixture are not chemically combined together. These substances can be:

- two or more elements
- two or more compounds
- elements and compounds.

Mixing does not change the chemical properties of each substance in a mixture.

Distillation

DISTILLATION is one of several physical methods that can be used to separate the substances in a mixture. It is used to separate a mixture of liquids that have dissolved into each other. The mixture is heated until one of the liquids evaporates. Its vapours are then cooled and condensed to form a separated liquid.

Fractional distillation

FRACTIONAL DISTILLATION is used to separate mixtures containing several different substances. It is used to separate crude oil into FRACTIONS in a continuous process.

Each fraction contains molecules with a similar number of carbon atoms and boiling point.

Fractional distillation of crude oil happens in a fractionating column:

The oil is heated to evaporate it.

Vapour from the oil rises up the column.

Each fraction condenses at a different temperature because it has a diferent range of boiling points.

Worked example D-C

The diagram shows the formula and boiling point of some alkanes in three fractions.

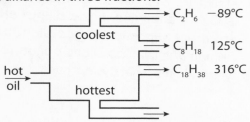

- coolest
- C_2H_6 $-89°C$
- C_8H_{18} $125°C$
- $C_{18}H_{38}$ $316°C$
- hot oil
- hottest

(a) How does the number of carbon atoms in an alkane affect its boiling point? *(1 mark)*

(a) The higher the number of carbon atoms in a molecule of alkane, the higher the boiling point.

(b) Explain which of these alkanes is the most flammable. *(2 marks)*

(b) C_2H_6, because it has the smallest molecules.

There are trends in the properties of the different fractions from crude oil.

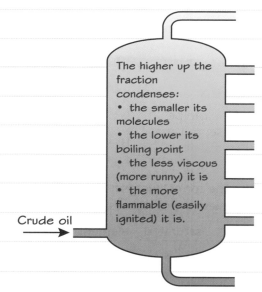

The higher up the fraction condenses:

- the smaller its molecules
- the lower its boiling point
- the less viscous (more runny) it is
- the more flammable (easily ignited) it is.

Crude oil

These properties influence how the fractions are used as fuels.

Now try this

1 State two properties of an alkane that depend on the number of carbon atoms in its molecules. *(2 marks)*

2 State the property of crude oil fractions that allows them to be separated during fractional distillation. *(1 mark)*

3 Describe how crude oil is separated by fractional distillation. *(3 marks)*

Combustion

Complete combustion

The combustion of hydrocarbon fuels releases energy to the surroundings. The hydrogen and carbon in the fuel reacts with oxygen and is OXIDISED. If there is plenty of oxygen, COMPLETE COMBUSTION occurs. The hydrogen in the fuel is oxidised to water vapour and the carbon is oxidised to carbon dioxide:

hydrogen + oxygen → water

carbon + oxygen → carbon dioxide

Partial combustion

If there is not enough oxygen, INCOMPLETE COMBUSTION (partial combustion) occurs. The hydrogen in the fuel is still oxidised to water vapour, but the carbon is not fully oxidised. These products are also formed:

- carbon monoxide
- particulates (solid particles).

The solid particles contain soot, which is carbon, and unburned fuel.

NO$_x$

NO$_x$ or OXIDES OF NITROGEN are formed (from nitrogen and oxygen in the air) at high temperatures, like those found in furnaces and car engines. They also cause ACID RAIN.

Sulfur dioxide

Most fuels naturally contain some sulfur. When the fuel burns, the sulfur oxidises to sulfur dioxide gas:

sulfur + oxygen → sulfur dioxide

Acid rain damages rocks, buildings, trees and aquatic life.

Sulfur dioxide pollution can be reduced by:

- Removing sulfur from the fuel.
- Removing sulfur dioxide after burning.

Worked example   target G-E

The diagram shows some of the substances released when fossil fuels are burned.

water vapour
carbon dioxide
sulfur dioxide
particulates

(a) Which of the substances released causes acid rain? *(1 mark)*

Sulfur dioxide

(b) Draw a ring around the correct answer to complete the sentence. *(1 mark)*

Particulates cause

- global warming
- rising sea levels
- ~~global dimming~~

Carbon dioxide is a cause of global **warming**, particulates reflect sunlight back into space causing global **dimming**.

Now try this

target G-E

1 Name the gas in the air that reacts with fuels when they burn. *(1 mark)*

2 State the environmental problem caused by sulfur dioxide and oxides of nitrogen. *(1 mark)*

target D-C

3 The table shows the products of combustion of two fuels, A and B.

Fuel	Carbon dioxide	Carbon monoxide	Water vapour	Sulfur dioxide
A	✓	✗	✓	✓
B	✗	✓	✗	✓

(a) Explain which fuel was a hydrocarbon. *(2 marks)*

(b) Explain which fuel underwent incomplete combustion. *(2 marks)*

Biofuels

Biofuels

BIOFUELS are produced from plant material rather than from fossil fuels. They release less carbon dioxide overall when burned.

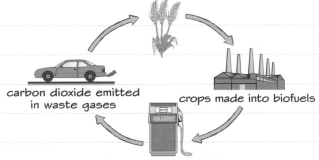

carbon dioxide absorbed in photosynthesis

carbon dioxide emitted in waste gases

crops made into biofuels

biofuels used by vehicles

Biodiesel and bioethanol

BIODIESEL and BIOETHANOL are biofuels.

- ✓ Biodiesel can be used in diesel engines.
- ✓ Bioethanol can be mixed with petrol and used in petrol engines.
- ✗ Farmland used for food production is used for biofuel production instead.

Both fuels are produced from renewable resources. However, non-renewable resources may be used indirectly:

- ✗ to make fertilisers for the plant crops
- ✗ to provide energy during their manufacture and transport.

Worked example   target D-C

SPEC AQA SKILL

The chart shows car exhaust emissions using diesel from crude oil, and using biodiesel.

Which fuel is better for the environment? Use your knowledge and the information above to help you answer the question.   *(3 marks)*

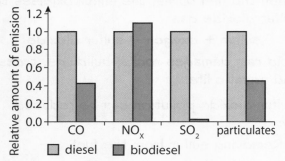

I think that generally biodiesel is better for the environment. Apart from the emissions of NO_x, emissions from biodiesel are lower than those from the ordinary diesel. The SO_2 emissions are reduced a lot more than the others. The reduction in particulates will reduce global dimming. Biodiesel releases less carbon dioxide overall than ordinary diesel does.

Hydrogen as a fuel

Water vapour is the only product made when hydrogen burns:

hydrogen + oxygen → water

- ✓ No carbon dioxide is made when hydrogen burns.
- ✓ Hydrogen can be made by passing electricity through water.
- ✗ most hydrogen is produced from fossil fuels at the moment
- ✗ electricity needed to make hydrogen from water may be generated by burning fossil fuels
- ✗ hydrogen is difficult to store and there are only a few places that sell it.

You may also be asked about the social and economic impacts of using fuels.

Now try this

1 Compare the products made when ethanol and hydrogen burn.   *(2 marks)*

target G-E

2 Biofuel crops are valuable to farmers but farmland is needed to grow them. Suggest one possible problem for the food supply if the use of biofuels increases.   *(1 mark)*

target D-C

Chemistry six mark question 2

There will be one 6 mark question on your exam paper which will be marked for *Quality of Written Communication as well as scientific knowledge*. This means that you need to apply your scientific knowledge, present your answer in a logical and organised way and make sure that your spelling, grammar and punctuation are as good as you can make them.

Worked example

SPEC AQA SKILL

Metals such as steel, copper and aluminium are made into many useful things, such as parts for cars. The raw materials for these metals are extracted from metal ores.

When they are no longer needed, items containing metals may be thrown away as waste, or they may be recycled.

Describe why it is important to recycle these metals rather than disposing of them in landfill sites. *(6 marks)*

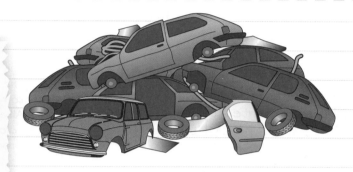

If we just throw away metal we will have to get more for the things we use. Metals are extracted from ores, which involves digging up and processing large amounts of rock. This produces a lot of waste and damages habitats. A lot of energy is needed to extract metals from their ores. For example, electricity is used to extract aluminium and to purify copper. This is expensive.

Recycling metals instead of mining for new ones means the ores will last longer. Fewer mines will be needed, which will reduce waste and loss of habitat. Fewer landfill sites will be needed, as there will be less waste. Less energy is needed to melt down a metal for recycling than is needed to extract it from its ore.

EXAM ALERT!

Make sure you plan your answer. This question asks you to about both recycling and landfill. Make sure that your answer contains information on both.

Students have struggled with questions like this in recent exams – **be prepared!**

This answer describes two environmental impacts of mining, followed by an economic impact of producing metals from their ores. The release of harmful gases might also have been mentioned. For example, carbon dioxide is released from the blast furnace when making iron. Generating electricity from fossil fuels also releases carbon dioxide.

Now try this

Aluminium and copper are both useful metals but they are extracted from their ores in different ways. Describe how aluminium and copper are extracted from their ores. *(6 marks)*

Think about how aluminium is extracted from aluminium oxide, and how copper is extracted from copper oxide. What steps are involved in each process?

Cracking and alkenes

Cracking is a reaction in which hydrocarbons are broken down to form smaller molecules, including alkanes and ALKENES. Some of these products are useful as fuels.

Cracking

CRACKING is a THERMAL DECOMPOSITION reaction. In cracking, oil fractions are heated so they vaporise. Their vapours are either:

- passed over a hot catalyst, or
- mixed with steam and heated to very high temperatures.

Alkenes

Alkenes are hydrocarbons. They are UNSATURATED because their molecules contain one or more carbon–carbon double bond.

Alkenes have the general formula C_nH_{2n}. For example, the chemical formula for butene (which contains four carbon atoms) is C_4H_8.

Formulae of alkenes

An alkene molecule can be represented by its CHEMICAL FORMULA or by its DISPLAYED STRUCTURE.

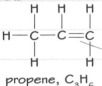

propene, C_3H_6

The = represents a double bond. The C=C bond allows alkenes to react with BROMINE WATER. Alkenes turn it from orange to colourless (alkanes cannot do this). Bromine water can be used as a test for unsaturated molecules.

ethene, C_2H_4

The names of alkenes end in 'ene'.

The hydrocarbon $C_{20}H_{42}$ was heated and its vapour passed over hot broken porcelain. This is one of the reactions that happened:

$$C_{18}H_{38} \rightarrow C_8H_{18} + C_8H_{16} + C_2H_4$$

(a) Write the formula of two alkenes in the reaction. *(2 marks)*

(b) Suggest two reasons why there is a greater demand for the products than for the original hydrocarbon. *(2 marks)*

(a) C_2H_4, C_8H_{16}

(b) Smaller hydrocarbons make better fuels than larger ones. Alkenes are used to make polymers.

Remember:

- alkanes – the number of H atoms is double the number of C atoms plus two
- alkenes – the number of H atoms is double the number of C atoms.

Compared to larger hydrocarbons, smaller alkanes and alkenes are less viscous (more runny), more flammable and have lower boiling points (they tend to be gas or liquid). They are more useful as fuels.

G–E

D–C

1 The diagram shows an experiment to crack paraffin soaked onto mineral wool.

   (a) State why the paraffin must be warmed. *(1 mark)*

   (b) Describe a lab test for the presence of alkenes at position X. *(2 marks)*

   (c) C_2H_4 molecules collect at position Y. Draw the displayed formula of C_2H_4. *(1 mark)*

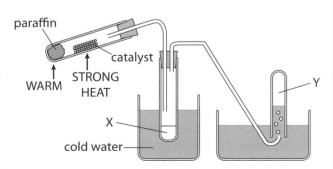

Making polymers

Alkenes can be used to make polymers (plastics).

Polymerisation

Alkene molecules can act as MONOMERS. They can join together in a POLYMERISATION reaction to make very large molecules called POLYMERS.

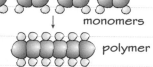

monomers

polymer

For example, ethene forms poly(ethene).

$$n \; C=C \;\rightarrow\; \left(C-C \right)_n$$

The displayed formulae show that many (*n*) ethene monomers can react together to form n units of poly(ethene).

(a) Complete this equation to show how a polymer forms from propene. *(1 mark)*

(b) Name the polymer formed. *(1 mark)*

(a)

$$n \; C=C \;\rightarrow\; \left(C-C \right)_n$$

(b) Poly(propene)

The name of a polymer is given by its monomer – it is poly(name of monomer).

EXAM ALERT!

You should be able to show the formation of a polymer from a given alkene monomer. Students have often struggled to do this in exams. They often forget to change the double bond to a single bond or they leave out the *n*.

Students have struggled with questions like this in recent exams – **be prepared!**

To convert from a monomer to a polymer:
- draw the monomer but with a single bond
- draw a long bond either side
- draw brackets through the long bonds
- write n after the bracket.

Uses of polymers

New polymers and uses of polymers are being developed. Polymers developed for one use may be used in new ways.

Polymers are being developed as medical dressings and shape memory polymers as well as:

hydrogels (for babies nappies)

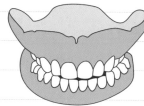

false teeth and fillings

Now try this

1 (a) Name the monomer that makes poly(ethene). *(1 mark)*

 (b) Name the process in which poly(ethene) is made. *(1 mark)*

2 The inside of babies' disposable nappies contains a powdered hydrogel underneath a lining layer. Suggest two properties the hydrogel should have. *(2 marks)*

3 (a) Complete this equation to show how a polymer forms from chloroethene. *(1 mark)*

 (b) Name the polymer formed. *(1 mark)*

$$n \; C=C \;\rightarrow$$

Polymer problems

Biodegradability

A BIODEGRADABLE material can be broken down by microbes. Many polymers are not biodegradable. Microbes cannot break them down and they do not rot. This is a useful property because items made from polymers last a long time and may be recycled. However, it makes disposing of polymers more difficult.

Biodegradable polymers

CORNSTARCH is a natural substance that microbes can break down. It is used for:

- making biodegradable polymers
- making plastic bags that break down more easily.

Landfill sites

Most waste is dumped in LANDFILL SITES:

- ✓ This is a cheap way of disposing of waste.
- ✓ Waste is out of sight once it is covered over.
- ✗ Space for landfill sites is running out.
- ✗ Most polymers are not biodegradable and will last for many years.
- ✗ Landfill sites are unsightly and attract pests.

Worked example

Give two advantages of recycling polymers.   *(2 marks)*

Recycling avoids filling up landfill sites, and avoids using up non-renewable resources (as polymers are made from crude oil).

There are disadvantages to recycling polymers as well. Recycling is expensive because the different polymers must be collected and sorted. Some polymers cannot be recycled.

Worked example

Read this newspaper report.

> **Selling plastic to China**
> Oil prices are rising. Some Chinese companies have started paying to have American and European waste polythene shipped to them.

Explain why it has become worthwhile for Chinese companies to pay for waste polythene.   *(2 marks)*

Polythene is made from crude oil. The cost of crude oil may have risen to the point where it is cheaper to recycle polythene instead.

Fuels vs. polymers

Most crude oil is used for fuel, but it is also used to make chemicals. These include medicines and paints, as well as polymers. Oil is a limited resource. It will run out one day if we keep using it. There are social, economic and environmental issues in the use of crude oil for different purposes.

This answer looks at the economic aspects of recycling polymers, but there are environmental and social aspects too. Recycling creates new jobs. These may not just be in the recycling industry, but in transport, for example.

Now try this

1 Many polymers are not biodegradable. State what this means.   *(1 mark)*

2 Give one advantage of making plastic bags from polymers and cornstarch.   *(1 mark)*

3 Suggest one reason why it may be better to recycle polymers, rather than to dispose of them in landfill sites.   *(2 marks)*

Ethanol

Ethanol is the alcohol in alcoholic drinks. It is also a fuel, and it has industrial and chemical uses. There are two ways to produce ethanol:

Fermentation

FERMENTATION is a natural process. It uses yeast (a type of microorganism) to convert sugar from plants into ethanol:

sugar → carbon dioxide + ethanol

Fermentation is used to make alcoholic drinks and most of the ethanol used as a fuel.

Hydration of ethane

Most ethanol for industrial use is made by hydration of ethene. Ethene and steam react together in the presence of a catalyst to make ethanol:

$$\begin{array}{c}\text{H} \quad \text{H} \\ | \quad\; | \\ \text{C}{=}\text{C} + \text{H}{-}\text{O}{-}\text{H} \rightarrow \text{H}{-}\text{C}{-}\text{C}{-}\text{O}{-}\text{H} \\ | \quad\; | \quad\quad\quad\quad\quad\; | \quad\; | \\ \text{H} \quad \text{H} \quad\quad\quad\quad\quad \text{H} \quad \text{H} \end{array}$$

Worked example   target D–C

SPEC AQA SKILL

Look at the information given below on the two different ways to produce ethanol. Suggest which method of producing ethanol would be better to use in a country with lots of land but not a lot of crude oil. Explain your answer.   *(2 marks)*

Fermentation
- Raw material (sugar) is renewable.
- Process doesn't need very high temperatures.
- Reaction is slow.
- Ethanol must be purified before use.
- Land to grow fuel crops could be used instead for food crops.

Hydration of ethene
- Raw material (crude oil) is non-renewable.
- Process needs high temperatures.
- Reaction is fast.
- Pure ethanol is made.
- Ethene is made by fractional distillation of oil, then cracking, which needs energy.

Fermentation would be better in this case because a country like this would have lots of land to grow the sugar but the oil would be too expensive to use to make ethene and then ethanol.

Now try this

 target G–E

1 Ethanol can be made by fermentation or by hydration of ethene.

   (a) Complete the word equation for fermentation: .... → .... + ethanol   *(2 marks)*

   (b) Name the substance that reacts with ethene to make ethanol.   *(1 mark)*

2 Tick (✓) two correct statements about making ethanol.   *(2 marks)*

target D–C

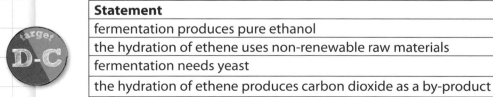

Statement	Tick (✓)
fermentation produces pure ethanol	
the hydration of ethene uses non-renewable raw materials	
fermentation needs yeast	
the hydration of ethene produces carbon dioxide as a by-product	

3 Suggest why most ethanol for use as fuel is produced by fermentation, rather than by hydration of ethene.   *(2 marks)*

Vegetable oils

There are two ways that oils can be extracted from seeds, nuts and fruits:

Pressing and filtering

The plant material must be crushed to release oil and water from the plant cells. The oil floats on top of the water and crushed plants.

vegetable oil
water
skin and seeds

The crushed plant material may need PRESSING to remove the oil. The crushed plant material can be removed by FILTRATION. The oil and water are separated to make a useful product.

Distillation

| water is boiled to create steam |
| steam passes through the plant material |
| the steam carries away the oil |
| the mixture of steam and oil is cooled |
| oil floats on the condensed steam |

Cooking with oils

Food can be cooked by boiling in water. Vegetable oils have higher boiling points than water. This means that food cooked in oil:

- ✓ cooks at higher temperatures
- ✓ cooks faster than in water
- ✓ has different flavours
- ✗ releases more energy when it is eaten.

Worked example   target D-C   SPEC AQA SKILL

The table shows the amount of energy in 100 g of three foods.

Food	Energy in kJ per 100 g
boiled potato	360
fried potato wedges	1180
potato crisps	2240

(a) Explain why the wedges and crisps contain more energy than the boiled potato. *(2 marks)*

(b) Suggest a possible health effect of eating crisps rather than boiled potato. *(1 mark)*

(a) They are cooked in oil, which increases the energy the food releases when eaten.

(b) You could become overweight.

In an exam you may be given data to evaluate. This usually means that you have to know some advantages and disadvantages. Vegetable oils are important foods because they provide us with nutrients and a lot of energy. However, too much can make us overweight, and this can cause health problems.

Now try this

target G-E

1 Tick (✓) two reasons why sunflower oil, not water, is used to cook potatoes to make crisps. *(2 marks)*

Statement	Tick (✓)
potato only cooks above the boiling point of water	
boiled potato is soft, not crisp	
sunflower oil is cheaper than water	
potatoes cook faster in sunflower oil	

2 Rapeseed seeds are crushed and pressed to release a liquid. State why rapeseed oil separates from water in the liquid after a few minutes. *(1 mark)*

target D-C

3 Describe two ways in which plant oil may be removed from crushed plant material. *(2 marks)*

Emulsions

Oils do not dissolve in water. If an oil and water are shaken together, they form a mixture called an EMULSION.

Compared to oil or water alone, emulsions:

- ✅ are thicker (more viscous)
- ✅ have better coating ability (they stick to food or other objects better)
- ✅ have a better texture and appearance.

This makes them useful for paints, salad dressings, ice cream and cosmetics.

Emulsifiers

An emulsion will eventually separate out again until all the oil is floating on the water. EMULSIFIERS are substances that make emulsions more STABLE (they do not separate out after mixing).

For example, the natural emulsifiers in egg yolk prevent the vinegar and oil in mayonnaise separating out after mixing.

 Worked example　　D-C

 SPEC AQA SKILL

Egg lecithin may be used as an emulsifier in food. Some people are allergic to eggs.

(a) Give an advantage of emulsifiers.　(1 mark)

(b) Suggest why egg lecithin may be listed as an ingredient on food labels.　(1 mark)

(a) Emulsifiers stop oil and water separating, which increases the shelf-life of the food.

(b) People allergic to eggs can decide whether they should eat the food.

Emulsifiers are important ingredients for making emulsions stable. On the other hand, some people may be allergic to them. The list of ingredients enables people to make informed decisions about whether to eat the food.

Unsaturated vegetable oils

Unsaturated oils are better for health than saturated oils and fats

- saturated vegetable oils only have carbon–carbon single bonds, C–C
- UNSATURATED vegetable oils have carbon–carbon double bonds, C=C, as well
- POLYUNSATURATED oils have many C=C bonds.

Testing for unsaturation

Bromine water is orange. It turns colourless when it is mixed with an unsaturated substance. The more C=C bonds there are, the more bromine water must be added before it stops becoming colourless.

Now try this

 target G-E

1　Salad dressing can be made by shaking olive oil with vinegar. The dressing separates after a while. Tick (✓) **one** reason why the olive oil forms a layer on top of the vinegar.　(1 mark)

Reason	Tick (✓)
water has a lower density than olive oil	
water has a lower boiling point than olive oil	
water does not dissolve olive oil	

2　(a) State the type of oil that contains carbon–carbon double bonds.　(1 mark)

　　(b) Describe what happens when bromine water is shaken with an unsaturated oil.　(2 marks)

 target D-C

3　Describe what an emulsifier does.　(2 marks)

The Earth's structure

The Earth has a layered structure.

Three main layers

The Earth is surrounded by an ATMOSPHERE and has three main layers.

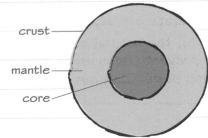

crust
mantle
core

The CRUST is the thinnest layer. The MANTLE is a thick layer between the crust and the core. The radius of the CORE is just over half the Earth's radius.

Tectonic plates

The Earth's crust and the upper part of the mantle are cracked into several very large pieces. These are called TECTONIC PLATES.

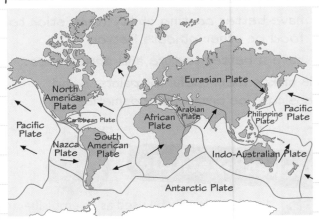

North American Plate
Pacific Plate
Nazca Plate
Caribbean Plate
South American Plate
African Plate
Arabian Plate
Eurasian Plate
Philippine Plate
Pacific Plate
Indo-Australian Plate
Antarctic Plate

Moving plates

The tectonic plates move at a few centimetres per year. They move because of CONVECTION CURRENTS in the mantle. These currents are driven by HEAT from natural RADIOACTIVE processes in the Earth.

The mantle is mostly solid but it can move slowly. Tectonic plates can move towards or away from each other. They can also move past each other. Most **Earthquakes** and **volcanoes** happen at the boundaries between plates.

Worked example   target D-C

SPEC AQA SKILL

Explain why scientists cannot accurately predict when an earthquake will occur. *(2 marks)*

Scientists cannot be sure what is happening under the crust, such as how big the forces are there. So although they know that earthquakes happen at plate boundaries, they cannot be sure exactly when.

EXAM ALERT!

Scientists understand the processes involved in earthquakes and volcanoes. However, earth movements can be sudden and disastrous, making it difficult to predict when they will happen.

Students have struggled with questions like this in recent exams – **be prepared!**

Now try this

target G-E

1 The Earth has a layered structure. Name parts A and B.   *(2 marks)*

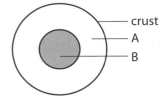

crust
A
B

target G-E

2 **(a)** About how fast do tectonic plates move?   *(1 mark)*

(b) Give two examples of geological events that happen where tectonic plates meet.   *(2 marks)*

3 Describe why tectonic plates move.   *(2 marks)*

target D-C

4 People living near a volcano may ignore scientists when they predict an eruption. Suggest a reason why.   *(1 mark)*

Continental drift

Alfred Wegener was a German scientist who proposed a theory of crustal movement, called CONTINENTAL DRIFT. It was not generally accepted for many years.

Shrinking Earth

Before Wegener, scientists thought that features on the Earth's surface were caused by it shrinking.

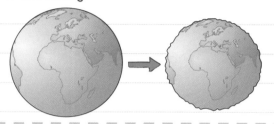

The idea was that as the Earth cooled after it was formed, its crust shrank and wrinkled to form mountains. The idea is now disproved.

Prediction: If this theory is correct then mountains should cover the Earth.

Observation: mountains are not everywhere.

Continental drift

Alfred Wegener suggested that all the Earth's land was once joined together, forming a 'supercontinent'. This broke up millions of years ago and the landmasses moved apart.

Wegener's ideas were based on observations involving South America and Africa.

Evidence for continental drift

Wegener's evidence for his theory included:

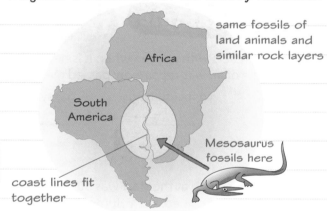

same fossils of land animals and similar rock layers

Africa

South America

coast lines fit together

Mesosaurus fossils here

Worked example   target D-C

When Wegener proposed his theory of continental drift in 1912, other scientists thought that he was wrong. Give one reason why they thought this.   *(1 mark)*

Wegener had no evidence to show how continents could move.

EXAM ALERT!

Make sure you give specific answers rather than just writing that Wegener had no evidence for his theory.

Students have struggled with questions like this in recent exams – **be prepared!**

Wegener was not a geologist. He had evidence to support his idea but couldn't explain how continents moved. Evidence that the continents are parts of moving tectonic plates was not discovered until much later.

Now try this

1 Give two pieces of evidence that South America and Africa were once joined together.   *(2 marks)*

2 Describe what Alfred Wegener meant by 'continental drift'.   *(2 marks)*

The Earth's atmosphere

The Earth's ATMOSPHERE has stayed much the same for the last 200 million years.

The two main gases in the atmosphere are nitrogen (about 4/5ths) and oxygen (about 1/5th). There are smaller amounts of other gases.

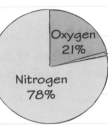

Oxygen 21%
Nitrogen 78%
other gases 1% including argon, water vapour and carbon dioxide

The early atmosphere

The Earth is 4.6 billion years old. There was intense volcanic activity during the first billion years of its existence. This activity:

• released gases that formed the early atmosphere
• released water vapour that cooled and condensed to form the oceans.

You should know the rough proportions of gases in the atmosphere today.

Worked example target D-C

Copper reacts with oxygen when it is heated. In an experiment, a sample of air was repeatedly passed over hot copper turnings.

copper turnings   gas syringe

HEAT

The volume of air at the start was 50 cm³. At the end, after the apparatus had cooled, the volume was 40 cm³. Calculate the percentage of oxygen in the air.   *(2 marks)*

volume of oxygen = 50 – 40 = 10 cm³
percentage of oxygen = 10/50 × 100 = 20%

Raw materials

Earth's atmosphere, crust and oceans are the only sources of the minerals and other resources needed by humans. For example, air is the raw material for producing oxygen for industrial and medical use.

You could be asked a question based on experiments but you will be given lots of information in the question. It is a good idea to look through your practical work as part of your revision.

Now try this

target G-E

1 The bar chart shows the amounts of different gases in air. Give the names of gases A and B.   *(2 marks)*

target D-C

2 Describe how volcanoes on the early Earth caused oceans to form.   *(2 marks)*

3 In an experiment to find the percentage of oxygen in air, 100 cm³ of air was repeatedly passed over hot copper turnings.

   (a) Write a word equation for the reaction.   *(1 mark)*

   (b) The volume at the end was 79 cm³. Calculate the percentage of oxygen.   *(2 marks)*

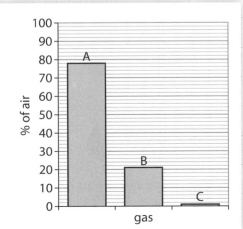

% of air vs gas

The early atmosphere

The Earth's atmosphere first formed a very long time ago, before humans evolved. As a result, there are several theories about how the atmosphere was formed and developed.

Mars

Venus

Early Earth

The atmosphere of Mars and Venus today are mostly carbon dioxide and contain little or no oxygen.

One theory of the early atmosphere suggests that it was similar to today's atmospheres of Mars and Venus, but with
- water vapour
- small proportions of methane and ammonia

Worked example   target G-E

SPEC AQA SKILL

Billions of years ago, the Earth's atmosphere was probably like the atmosphere of Mars today. The table shows the atmospheres of the Earth and Mars today.

Use information from the table to describe how the Earth's atmosphere today is different from its atmosphere billions of years ago. *(2 marks)*

	% of atmosphere	
Gas	**Earth**	**Mars**
nitrogen	78.1	2.7
oxygen	20.9	0.1
argon	0.9	1.6
carbon dioxide	0.04	95.3

There is very much more nitrogen and oxygen than there was billions of years ago, and there is a lot less carbon dioxide than there was.

The answer compares the amounts of each gas, rather than just repeating data in the table. The percentage of argon is almost the same.

Life on Earth

There are many theories to explain how life formed on Earth billions of years ago, but living things cause changes to the Earth's atmosphere. For example, plants and algae produced the oxygen that is in today's atmosphere.

Photosynthesis

Plants and algae make their own food by a process called PHOTOSYNTHESIS. This process:
- uses energy from sunlight
- releases oxygen into the atmosphere
- uses carbon dioxide from the atmosphere.

Now try this

target G-E

1 (a) What is photosynthesis? *(1 mark)*

(b) Name the gas released during photosynthesis. *(1 mark)*

2 The atmosphere of Venus today is 96.5% carbon dioxide, 3.5% nitrogen and small amounts of oxygen and argon. Describe differences between the atmospheres of Earth and Venus today. *(2 marks)*

target D-C

3 State and explain the change in the percentage of oxygen in the Earth's atmosphere from the early Earth to today. *(3 marks)*

The early atmosphere and carbon dioxide

The presence of living organisms on Earth has made huge changes to the composition of the Earth's atmosphere over billions of years.

Carbon dioxide levels

As the Earth's atmosphere has developed
- carbon dioxide levels have gone down
- oxygen levels have gone up.

Photosynthesis by plants and algae is one reason for these changes.

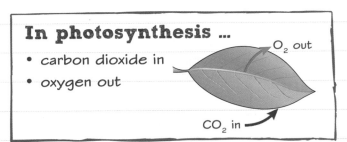

In photosynthesis ...
- carbon dioxide in
- oxygen out

O_2 out

CO_2 in

Fossil fuels

FOSSIL FUELS formed over millions of years from the remains of dead plants and animals. The carbon they contain originally came from the atmosphere when the organisms were alive. Carbon dioxide was 'locked up' in fossil fuels as:

- carbon in coal
- HYDROCARBONS in oil and natural gas.

Coal is a type of SEDIMENTARY ROCK.

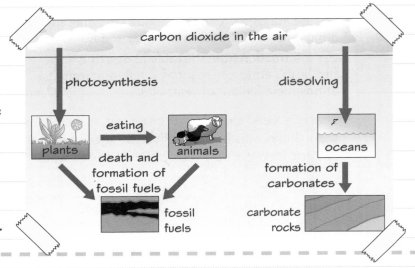

carbon dioxide in the air

photosynthesis

dissolving

plants

eating

animals

death and formation of fossil fuels

oceans

fossil fuels

formation of carbonates

carbonate rocks

Worked example   D-C

The oceans have an important part to play in absorbing carbon dioxide from the atmosphere. Describe the processes involved. *(3 marks)*

Carbon dioxide dissolves in the oceans. It forms carbonates, which sea creatures use to make their shells and skeletons. These form limestone rock when the animals die and their shells sink to the seabed.

Now try this

D-C

1   The diagram shows natural processes that involve carbon dioxide.

Describe four ways in which carbon dioxide can be removed from the atmosphere.

(4 marks)

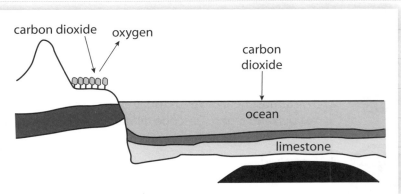

carbon dioxide   oxygen

carbon dioxide

ocean

limestone

Carbon dioxide today

Human activities are releasing gases into the atmosphere, causing changes to its composition.

An ocean reservoir

Carbon dioxide is SOLUBLE in water. This is why carbon dioxide from the atmosphere DISSOLVES in the oceans.

The oceans contain a lot of water, so they act as a huge RESERVOIR for carbon dioxide.

Acidic solution

Carbon dioxide dissolves in water to form an ACIDIC solution. When the oceans absorb carbon dioxide, the pH of the water is reduced (it becomes more acidic). This affects the environment in the oceans.

Worked example target D-C

SPEC AQA SKILL

Explain why levels of carbon dioxide in the atmosphere are changing.

Fossil fuels release carbon dioxide when they burn. The use of fossil fuels is increasing the level of carbon dioxide in the atmosphere.

Extra carbon dioxide has negative impacts:
• acidification of the oceans
• global warming.

Changing atmosphere

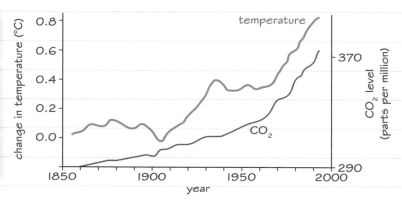

As the level of carbon dioxide in the atmosphere has risen, so has the average global temperature.

Worked example target D-C

(a) Choose the correct words from the box below to complete the word equation. *(1 mark)*

| oxygen   hydrogen   carbon dioxide |

carbonate + acid → <u>carbon dioxide</u> + salt + water

(b) Calcium carbonate is the major component of seashells. Carbon dioxide increases the acidity of seawater. Suggest a problem this may cause marine organisms. *(1 mark)*

Their shells may react with the acid in the water and wear away.

The oceans absorb carbon dioxide released into the atmosphere when fossil fuels are used. However, as this happens, the acidity of the water increases. This has an impact on marine organisms with shells.

Now try this

target G-E

1 Name two gases released during the complete combustion of fossil fuels. *(2 marks)*

2 State one consequence of an increase in the level of carbon dioxide in the atmosphere. *(1 mark)*

3 (a) State why the oceans are described as being a 'reservoir' for carbon dioxide. *(1 mark)*

target D-C

(b) Describe one reason why human activities are increasing the amount of carbon dioxide in the atmosphere. *(1 mark)*

(c) Describe one impact on the marine environment of the oceans absorbing extra amounts of carbon dioxide. *(1 mark)*

Chemistry six mark question 3

There will be one 6 mark question on your exam paper which will be marked for *Quality of Written Communication as well as scientific knowledge*. This means that you need to apply your scientific knowledge, present your answer in a logical and organised way and make sure that your spelling, grammar and punctuation are as good as you can make them.

Worked example

The table shows information about different hydrocarbon fractions in a sample of crude oil.

The supply is the amount of each fraction in the crude oil. The demand is the amount that can be sold. Fractional distillation of the crude oil produces too much of some fractions but too little of other fractions. Cracking can be used to reduce this problem.

| | Amount in tonnes | | Molecule size |
Fraction	Supply	Demand	
gases	8	8	smallest
petrol	16	26	
diesel	14	20	
kerosene	15	9	
heavy oil	20	15	
bitumen	36	24	largest

Describe the conditions needed for cracking. Use information from the table to explain which fractions should undergo cracking. *(6 marks)*

Cracking involves heating a fraction so that its hydrocarbons vaporise. The vapours are passed over a hot catalyst or mixed with steam and heated to very high temperatures.

In cracking, large hydrocarbon molecules produce smaller, more useful hydrocarbon molecules. The table shows that the demand for petrol and diesel is greater than the supply. On the other hand, the supply of bitumen and heavy oil is greater than the demand. These fractions should be cracked to make more petrol and diesel.

The first part of the question is answered here. Make sure you answer the whole question — here it would be easy to concentrate on the table and to forget this is needed.

The answer describes what cracking does so that it becomes clear why cracking is needed. Information from the table is used to explain which fractions should be chosen. You could quote numbers but you would still need to explain what they mean.

Now try this

The Earth has a layered structure. Its surface is broken into large pieces called tectonic plates, which are constantly moving. Explain how these tectonic plates move and describe the possible results of this movement. *(6 marks)*

The command word EXPLAIN means you need to make something clear or state reasons for it happening.

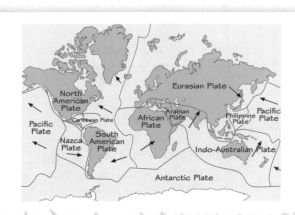

Infrared radiation

The amount of INFRARED RADIATION emitted or absorbed by an object depends on its temperature and its surface.

All objects EMIT and ABSORB infrared radiation. The hotter an object is, the more infrared radiation it gives out in a given period of time.

> emit means 'gives out';
> absorb means 'takes in'.

Colours and radiation

Surface properties of object	Radiation emitter	Radiation absorber
Dark, matt	good	good
Light, shiny	poor	poor

Light, shiny objects are also good REFLECTORS of infrared radiation.

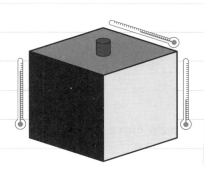

> The sides of the cube are at the same temperature but the thermometer near the dark, matt surface shows the highest temperature because the most radiation is emitted from the surface.

Worked example   D-C

 SPEC AQA SKILL

1 Compare the rate at which radiation is emitted by a cup of cold water and a hot cup of tea. *(2 marks)*

2 Explain why it might be a good idea to paint radiators in a house matt black. *(2 marks)*

> It is important to give a time (e.g. per second) when comparing the *rate* at which radiation is emitted.

1 They both give out infrared radiation but the hot cup of tea gives out more radiation every second.

2 The black radiators will give out more heat because black and matt objects are good emitters of infrared radiation.

EXAM ALERT!

'Explain' means to give a reason for something, so the answer usually has 'because' in it.

Students have struggled with questions like this in recent exams – **be prepared!**

Now try this

 target G-E

1 The following objects are all the same size. Which one emits radiation at the highest rate? Draw a ring around the correct answer. *(1 mark)*

  A: a lump of ice   B: a saucepan of boiling water   C: a bowl of cold water

target D-C

2 A student wants to make a cheap solar panel to heat water in his shed. The Sun will heat the water running through tubes in the panel. The hardware store sells plastic tubing in black, white and brown. Suggest which tubes he should use and give a reason for your answer. *(2 marks)*

Kinetic theory

The kinetic theory says that objects are made up of PARTICLES that are constantly moving.

Properties of matter

The KINETIC THEORY can be used to explain the properties of SOLIDS, LIQUIDS and GASES.

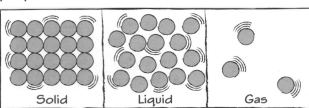

Solid   Liquid   Gas

Solids: **particles** can just **vibrate** about fixed positions. Solids have a fixed shape.

Liquids: Particles move around but stay close togaether. Liquids can flow.

Gases: Particles move fast and have lots of space between them. Gases fill a container and can flow.

Changes of state

When particles in a solid are given more energy they can start to move around and become a liquid.

When particles in a liquid are given more energy they move apart and become a gas.

Particles in a gas have more energy than particles in a liquid, and particles in a liquid have more energy than particles in a solid.

The amount of energy a particle has is related to the temperature of the material.

Worked example

target **D-C**

Match the properties of solids, liquids and gases to the explanations using the kinetic theory. *(4 marks)*

Property		Explanation
A solid has a fixed shape		There is a lot of space between the particles
Liquids take up the shape of the container they are in		The particles do not move around, only vibrate
Gases can be compressed into a smaller volume		Particles in liquids have more energy than in the solid
		Particles can move to new positions

EXAM ALERT!

You should be able to recognise the states from diagrams showing the particles.

Students have struggled with questions like this in recent exams – **be prepared!**

Now try this

target **D-C**

1 A teacher holds a clear plastic box containing some beads. When he holds the box still the beads lie at the bottom close together.

   (a) Which state is modelled by the beads in the box?   *(1 mark)*

   (b) Suggest what the teacher must do to model what happens to particles in a liquid.   *(2 marks)*

   (c) Suggest what the teacher would do to show the particles in a gas if the temperature rose.   *(1 mark)*

Methods of transferring energy

Energy is transferred from one place to another by CONDUCTION, CONVECTION, RADIATION, EVAPORATION and CONDENSATION.

Conduction

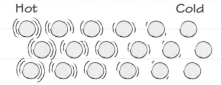

Hot   Cold

When particles in a solid are given more energy they vibrate more. They collide with neighbouring particles, which causes these particles to vibrate more. In this way energy spreads through the solid. In metals there are free electrons that help transfer the energy, making metals good conductors.

Convection

When particles in a liquid or gas are given more energy, they move faster and spread out. The density is lower so the hot material rises. It is replaced by cooler material, so a convection current is set up.

Radiation

Particles give out infrared radiation.

See page 69 for more on radiation.

Evaporation and condensation

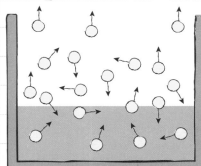

high energy: evaporating

medium energy: pulled back into water

lower energy: remain as liquid

The fastest-moving particles on the surface of a liquid escape as a gas. This is called evaporation. The average energy of the remaining particle is less, so the remaining liquid is cooler.

If energy is transferred from particles in a gas the particles will form droplets of liquid. This is called condensation.

Worked example   G-E

1 An egg is being cooked in a saucepan full of hot water. Complete the following sentences using the words from the box.

| conduction particles electrons insulator |

(a) Energy is transferred through the saucepan by <u>conduction</u>.

(b) The saucepan is made of metal. Metal is a good conductor because free <u>electrons</u> pass energy through the metal easily.

(c) Energy is not transferred quickly through the plastic handle because plastic is an <u>insulator</u>.

(d) An insulator does not pass energy easily through it because its <u>particles</u> collide with each other less frequently.   *(4 marks)*

Now try this

 G-E

1 Suggest three ways to reduce the energy transfer from a mug containing a hot drink. *(3 marks)*

Think about ways of reducing conduction, convection, radiation and evaporation.

 D-C

2 Perfume or aftershave lotion feels cold when you put it on your skin. Explain why this happens.   *(3 marks)*

Rate of energy transfer

Energy transfer can be speeded up or slowed down by changing the materials or the design of an object.

Factors affecting energy transfer

The bigger the temperature difference between an object and its surroundings the faster energy is transferred.

The rate at which energy is transferred to or from the object depends on:

- The material from which the object is made or the material it is packed in. Insulators transfer heat more slowly.
- The surface area and volume of the object. Greater surface area means faster rate of energy transfer.
- The properties of the surface of the object. Dull, dark surfaces emit or absorb radiation at a higher rate.

Evaporation

Evaporation takes place faster when the temperature is higher, there is a large surface area in contact with the air, or when wind blows the water vapour away.

Condensation is the opposite of evaporation, so it happens faster if the temperature is low.

Polar bears

Polar bears keep warm with thick fur. The fur traps air so less energy is lost by convection. The fur is white so it radiates energy at a lower rate.

Tea keeps warm in a vacuum flask for several hours but would be cold in a cup after a few minutes.

Explain how the flask reduces the rate of energy transfer. *(2 marks)*

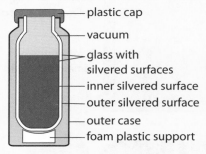

plastic cap
vacuum
glass with silvered surfaces
inner silvered surface
outer silvered surface
outer case
foam plastic support

The inside of the flask is silvered to reduce energy transferred by radiation. There is no gas between the layers of glass so energy cannot be transferred by convection. The plastic used to make the outside of the flask is an insulator so there is less energy transfer through conduction.

Now try this

 G-E

1 It is important that a motorbike engine does not get too hot. It has fins that transfer the energy to the air at a high rate. Why are the fins made of metal and why do they have a large surface area? *(2 marks)*

D-C

2 Explain why washing dries on a clothes line quicker on warm, windy days. *(2 marks)*

EXAM ALERT!

Remember that energy is never 'lost'. But when energy is transferred it is often 'wasted'.

Students have struggled with questions like this in recent exams – **be prepared!**

Keeping warm

Radiators are one way of warming a house up, but once it is warm then it is important that the house is insulated or the energy will be transferred to the surroundings and the house will cool down again. U-values are useful in choosing how to insulate your home.

Worked example

 The diagram shows a metal radiator that transfers 600 J of energy to the surroundings every second. Which features of the radiator allow it to transfer energy to the surroundings? *(3 marks)*

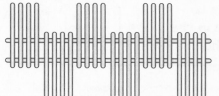

The radiator is made of a metal, to conduct heat from the hot water inside it. It has a large surface area that increases the rate of heat transfer to the air. However, it is a pale colour silver which reduces the radiation of energy.

U-values

Energy is transferred through a material when the temperature on each side is different.

U-values compare how much energy is transferred through materials in a given time. The values are for a given thickness and area of material.

The lower the U-value, the better the material is as an insulator. Metals have high U-values. Wool and foams have low U-values.

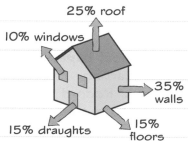

This picture shows how energy is usually lost from a house. Using materials with lower U-values can cut the amount of energy transferred.

Worked example

 Use the information in the table to answer the questions.

Material	U-value (10 cm thick)	Cost (£ per m²)	Payback time (years)
sheepwool	0.33	23	2.5
rockwool	0.20	38	2

A home owner decides to use rockwool to insulate her house because she thinks it is most cost-effective. Do you agree with this statement? Explain your answer. *(3 marks)*

'Payback time' is the number of years taken for the savings on energy bills to cover the cost of the insulation. Payback time = cost of the improvement/money saved each year.

Rockwool is the best insulator because it has the lowest U-value. It is more expensive to buy but has shorter payback time, so is more cost-effective.

Now try this

 1 The U-value for a wall with an air-filled cavity is 1.6. If the cavity is filled with foam the U-value becomes 0.5.

    (a) Explain the change in the U-value when the cavity is filled. *(2 marks)*

    (b) It costs £270 to fill the cavities in the walls of a house. The energy costs are reduced by £90 per year. Calculate the payback time for filling the cavities. *(2 marks)*

Specific heat capacity

Different amounts of energy are needed to change the temperature of different materials.

The SPECIFIC HEAT CAPACITY of a material is the amount of energy needed to raise the temperature of 1 kg of the material by 1°C.

The equation is $E = m \times c \times \theta$

- E is the energy transferred in joules (J)
- m is the mass of the material in kilograms (kg)
- c is the specific heat capacity in J/kg°C
- θ is the temperature change in °C.

Solar panels

Solar panels on roofs use the Sun's energy to heat water. The hot water can be used for washing or to heat the house.

The panels contain pipes. Cold water enters the pipes and is heated up by energy from the Sun. This energy passes from the heated water to cooler water in the tank overnight.

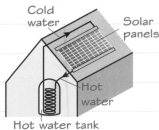

Cold water
Solar panels
Hot water
Hot water tank

Measuring specific heat capacity

To measure the specific heat capacity measure the mass and starting temperature of the block. Record how much energy is supplied to the block to produce a rise of 5°C.

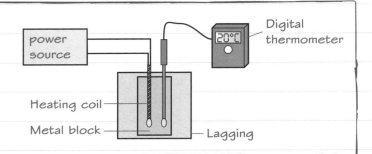

power source
Digital thermometer
Heating coil
Metal block
Lagging

Worked example target D-C

SPEC AQA SKILL

1 A solar water heating system heats 80 kg of water from 20°C to 60°C.

Calculate the amount of energy transferred to the hot water. The specific heat capacity of water is 4200 J/kg°C. *(3 marks)*

1 $E = m \times c \times \theta$

$E = 80\,kg \times 4200\,J/kg°C \times 40°C$

$= 13\,440\,000\,J$

Make sure that you are using the correct units for the quantities you use in calculations.

2 A shop sells two types of electric radiators. One is filled with 5 kg of water and the other is filled with 5 kg of oil (specific heat capacity of water is 4200 J/kg°C, of oil is 1900 J/kg°C).

Explain which of the radiators will stay warm for longer when electricity is turned off. *(2 marks)*

2 The water-filled radiator will stay warm for longer. It stores more energy because water has a higher specific heat capacity

---

Now try this

target D-C

1 A cook is using an aluminium saucepan, a copper saucepan and an iron saucepan. He heats the same amount of water in each pan and the pans all have the same mass. The water starts at the same temperature each time and the same hotplate is used to heat all three (specific heat capacities; aluminium 900 J/kg°C, copper 390 J/kg°C, iron 460 J/kg°C).

(a) Explain why the copper saucepan reaches 100°C first and the aluminium saucepan is last. *(2 marks)*

(b) If the saucepans each have a mass of 1.2 kg, calculate the energy needed to heat the iron saucepan from 20°C to 100°C. *(2 marks)*

Energy and efficiency

Energy cannot be created or destroyed, but it can be:

- stored
- transferred into useful forms
- dissipated.

For example, a light bulb transfers electrical energy to light but some of the energy is dissipated.

> **Dissipated** means the energy spreads out, making the surroundings warmer. It is 'wasted' energy.

EXAM ALERT!

The width of the arrows represents the amount of each type of energy. Make sure you can draw a Sankey diagram and understand what a Sankey diagram shows.

Students have struggled with questions like this in recent exams – **be prepared!**

Worked example   D-C

SPEC AQA SKILL

Sankey diagrams show energy transfers. A kettle is supplied with 200 kJ of electrical energy. 160 kJ of the energy raises the temperature of the water in the kettle.

(a) Explain what happens to the remaining energy. *(2 marks)*

(b) Sketch a Sankey diagram for the energy transfers in the kettle. *(3 marks)*

(c) Calculate the efficiency of the kettle.

(a) The energy is lost as waste energy, which warms up the surroundings.

(b)

Electrical energy input 200 kJ → Useful energy output 160 kJ

Wasted energy output 40 kJ

(c) efficiency = 160 kJ/200 kJ = 0.8

Efficiency

$$\text{Efficiency} = \frac{\text{useful energy out}}{\text{total energy in}} \text{ or } \frac{\text{useful power out}}{\text{total power in}}$$

> Multiply these figures by 100 to give them as a percentage. Remember, nothing has an efficiency of greater than 1, or 100%.

$$\text{Payback time} = \frac{\text{cost of new appliance}}{\text{cost of energy saved each year}}$$

> A shorter payback time makes the replacement more cost-effective.

Payback time is the time taken for the cost of a more efficient appliance to be paid by reduced energy bills.

Now try this

G-E

D-C

1 A plasma TV screen is supplied with 80 J of energy. 60 J is transferred as heat energy, making the surroundings warmer.

    (a) Draw a Sankey diagram to show the energy transfers in the TV. *(2 marks)*

    (b) Give one way that the energy supplied to the television is transferred usefully. *(1 mark)*

2 Calculate the efficiency of the plasma screen TV in the question above. *(2 marks)*

3 A family wants to replace their washing machine. Discuss the advantages of replacing it with a more efficient model. *(2 marks)*

Physics six mark question 1

There will be one 6 mark question on your exam paper which will be marked for *Quality of Written Communication as well as scientific knowledge*. This means that you need to apply your scientific knowledge, present your answer in a logical and organised way and make sure that your spelling, grammar and punctuation are as good as you can make them.

Worked example

A coffee shop wants to provide its customers with a cup that will keep a drink hot for longer.

Explain the ways that energy transfer from a cup of hot drink could be reduced.   *(6 marks)*

Energy is transferred from an open cup containing a hot drink in various ways.

- Conduction. Energy is transferred from the hot drink into the solid material of the cup and then into the hand holding it. Conduction happens when vibrating particles collide and transfer energy to neighbouring particles. Plastics and paper are poor conductors so should be used for the cup.

- Convection. Energy is transferred to particles of air when they hit a hot surface. Warm air rises and more cold air is drawn in to replace it. Convection can be decreased by trapping the air, such as by fitting a lid.

- Radiation. Hot objects give off more infrared radiation than cold objects. A white or silver cup would emit less radiation than a dark one.

Bullet points

You can use bullet points to structure your answer, but don't just write out a list. The bullet points should contain whole sentences.

As well as the three ways mentioned you could also give evaporation as an example. The faster-moving particles escape from the drink, leaving slower ones behind, so the drink cools. A lid will stop this happening.

Now try this

Use the data in the table to explain the advantages and disadvantages of replacing all the single glazed windows in a house with double glazed windows.   *(6 marks)*

	U-value	Cost (£)	Annual reduction in energy bill (£)	Payback time (years)
Cavity brick wall	1.8			
Single-glazed windows	5.0	2000	0	
Double-glazed windows	2.0	5000	250	20

Electrical appliances

The cost of using electrical appliances can be worked out if we know the amount of energy transferred in a given time.

Energy transferred (J)   =   power (W)   ×   time (s)
E   =   P   ×   t

The cost of electricity supplied by the mains is in pence per kilowatt-hour. Kilowatt-hours can be calculated like this:

Energy transferred (kilowatt-hours) = power (kilowatts) × time (hours)

> Take care! **Watts (W)** are a unit of power, but **kilowatt-hours (kWh)** are a unit of energy.

Energy transfers

Electrical appliances carry out many different energy transfers.

Light bulbs, display screens: electricity → light
Kettles, heaters: electricity → energy transfer by heating
Motors: electricity → kinetic energy
Radios: electricity → sound energy

Worked example

(a) Use the meter readings to calculate the amount of electrical energy supplied between 9 a.m. and 9 p.m.   *(1 mark)*

(b) Electrical energy costs 12p per kilowatt-hour. Calculate the cost of the electrical energy that was used.   *(2 marks)*

(a) 7460 kWh – 7445 kWh = 15 kWh (1)
(b) 15 kWh × 12p = 180p or £1.80

7 4 4 5 (kWh)   7 4 6 0 (kWh)
9 a.m.   9 p.m.

> Electricity meters measure the amount of electrical energy supplied to all the appliances in a building. Read the meter at the start and end of a period of time to find out how much electrical energy is being transferred by the appliances.

Worked example

A tumble dryer uses 1.5 kW of electrical power and runs for 2 hours.
How much electrical energy does the tumble dryer use.   *(2 marks)*

E = 1.5 kW × 2 h = 3 kWh

Now try this

1 A mobile phone has a battery that provides electrical energy at a rate of 3 W.

Which of the following are the useful energy transfers that take place in the phone. Put a tick next to those that you think apply.   *(1 mark)*

Energy transfer	Tick (✓)
Electrical energy → sound energy	
Electrical energy → heat energy	
Electrical energy → light energy	

2 (a) The mobile phone in the question above is used for four minutes. Calculate the amount of electrical energy transferred by the phone.   *(2 marks)*

(b) The battery is recharged using a mains charger with a power of 0.04 kW. It takes 2 hours to charge up fully. Electricity costs 12p per kilowatt-hour. Calculate the cost of charging the phone.   *(3 marks)*

Choosing appliances

Some electrical appliances are more suitable than others for certain applications.

More efficient appliances use less electricity, so they cost less to use. The higher efficiency may be due to stopping energy transfer to or from the appliance by improving the insulation around it. Kettles can be used more efficiently by only using them to heat the amount of water needed.

No mains supply?

In some places, cuts in the electricity supply are common while in others there is no mains electricity supply at all. Electrical energy has to be provided from generators using fossil fuels or a renewable source of energy.

Worked example

 D-C

 SPEC AQA SKILL

> A uses 3 kWh and B 2.2 kWh to toast 100 slices.

1 The manager of a busy cafe thinks that toaster B is the better appliance. Suggest reasons why he is correct. *(2 marks)*

Toaster	Electrical power used (kW)	Time to toast 100 slices
A	1.5	2 hours
B	2.2	1 hour

Toaster B is faster and although it uses more electrical power, it costs less to run.

2 An emergency medical centre is in a region where there is no electricity supply. Discuss how the centre can provide electrical energy for essential appliances. *(3 marks)*

Electrical energy could be supplied by batteries. The electrical energy for recharging the batteries could be supplied by generators burning a fuel by or by solar collectors during the day, or by wind turbines.

> Remember that renewable sources may be unreliable or not available all day, so electrical energy must be stored, most probably in batteries.

Now try this

 target G-E

1 A scientist compared refrigerators used in places where the electricity supply is unreliable. Medicines stored in the fridge must be kept below 6°C. The graph shows the temperature inside the refrigerators after the power is turned off. The refrigerators are the same size.

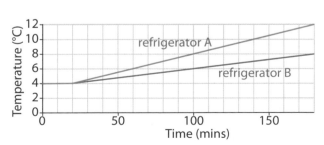

Use the graph to work out how long the medicines would be below 6°C after the electricity was cut off in each fridge. *(2 marks)*

 target D-C

2 (a) Explain the differences in the graph for the two refrigerators. *(2 marks)*

(b) Suggest one way to make a refrigerator more useful for keeping medicines cool. *(1 mark)*

Generating electricity

Most of our electricity is generated using power stations that turn water into steam.

Power station fuels

Energy sources for power stations include:

- FOSSIL FUELS (coal, oil, natural gas)
- NUCLEAR FISSION (the nuclei of uranium or plutonium atoms split up, releasing a lot of energy)
- BIOFUELS (fuels obtained from organisms, such as wood, straw, ethanol, oil palm, gas from rotting waste).

Supplies of some fossil fuels (oil and gas) will only last a few more decades. Fossil fuels, uranium and plutonium are NON-RENEWABLE sources of energy.

Accidents in nuclear power stations are rare but very costly. Nuclear power stations are expensive to build and very expensive to close down (decommission).

 Growing biofuels uses up land that could be used to grow food.

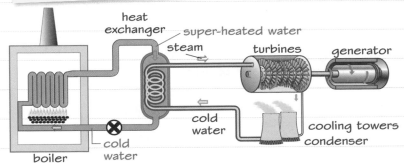

heat exchanger — super-heated water
steam — turbines — generator
cold water — cooling towers — condenser
cold water — boiler

Worked example   D-C

 SPEC AQA SKILL

Source of energy	% of electricity generated in the UK	Cost (p/kWh)	Cost to build (£/kW)	Lifetime of power station (years)	Time to start/stop
coal	43	10.5	1800	45	medium
natural gas	41	8	700	30	short
nuclear	15	9.9	3000	60	long

Refer to the table to answer the following questions.

(a) A politician says that burning coal is the cheapest method of generating electrical energy. Is this statement true? Explain your answer.   *(2 marks)*

(b) Suggest **two** reasons why nuclear power stations are kept running nearly all the time.   *(2 marks)*

(c) Explain why natural gas is used to top up the electricity supply when demand is highest.   *(2 marks)*

(a) It is not true. Gas-fired power stations are cheaper to build and gas is cheaper than coal, although the power stations do have to be replaced more often.

(b) Nuclear power stations take a long to time to start and stop, so it is better to keep them running. The cost of generating electricity is relatively low.

(c) Natural gas can supply electrical energy when needed because it has the shortest start-up time.

Now try this

 target G-E

1 Which of the following is a biofuel fuel that is burned to generate electricity?

A: coal   B: wood   C: natural gas   *(1 mark)*

2 Write down the stages in generating electricity from coal in a power station.   *(3 marks)*

 target D-C

3 Nuclear power stations have much lower fuel costs than coal-fired stations. Suggest why the cost of electricity from nuclear energy is almost the same as for coal.   *(2 marks)*

Renewables

Renewable sources of energy can also be used to generate electricity.

Renewable sources of energy

Wind: Turbines drive electricity generators. They are expensive because a huge number are needed. The wind is unreliable as it does not always blow, but the turbines require little maintenance.

Hydroelectricity: Falling water from reservoirs or rivers turns turbines to run generators. It is a fairly reliable source because rainwater can be stored and used when needed, but dams are very expensive to build.

Tides: Seawater can be trapped behind a barrage at high tide and used to turn turbines. Tidal currents can also be used to turn turbines placed underwater. The tides are predictable and reliable but barrages are very expensive to construct.

Waves: The rise and fall of waves is used to turn turbines. The height of the waves is unpredictable and the machinery needed has not been tested to see how much maintenance is required.

Geothermal: In some volcanic areas hot water and steam from deep underground can be used to drive turbines. The energy is available whenever it is needed but there are not many sites where it is available.

Solar: Solar cells turn sunlight directly into electricity. The cells are fitted to roofs or set up in fields to form 'solar farms'. Solar cells are expensive and only turn about 20% of the sun's energy into electricity. They only work in day time and when the sky is clear, but they need very little maintenance and can be used almost anywhere.

No National Grid?

Solar cells and small wind turbines are used to provide power for road signs. Small-scale hydroelectric generators are used in remote communities. In both cases it is too expensive to connect the generators to the National Grid.

Worked example   target D-C

SPEC AQA SKILL

A pumped storage scheme uses spare electrical energy to pump water to a high reservoir when the demand for electricity is low (for example, at night). At other times the water drives hydroelectric generators. Explain why this method is used.   *(2 marks)*

Electricity is difficult to store, so instead the electricity is used at quiet times to pump water. When the demand for electricity is high the water can be released to turn turbines and generate electricity for the country.

Electrical energy can only be stored in batteries, which are very expensive.

Now try this

target E-D

target E-C

1 A family living in a remote farmhouse uses about 10 kWh a day of electrical energy. They have a system of solar cells that can produce up to 10 kWh a day.

   (a) Explain why the solar cells may not provide electrical energy when the family needs it.   *(2 marks)*

   (b) Suggest ways that the family could ensure they have sufficient electrical energy.   *(3 marks)*

Environment and energy

Generating electricity in various ways has damaging effects on the environment.

You do not need to recall the details of the greenhouse effect and global warming at this stage.

Burning fuels releases pollutants into the atmosphere. Carbon dioxide contributes to global warming and climate change. Other substances cause acid rain.

Burning solid fuels (coal, wood) produces ash, which must be disposed of.

Noise pollution may be a disadvantage of wind farms. Mines are also noisy.

Environmental effects of using energy resources

Habitats can be destroyed by mining and oil and gas collection. Farming biofuels destroys natural habitats. Hydroelectric schemes and tidal barrages can cause habitats to be damaged.

Coal mines, oil rigs, power stations and wind farms are thought by some people to be visual pollution.

Nuclear power stations take up a lot less space than stations that burn coal because they do not need space for storing fuel. Wind farms cover many square kilometres to produce the same amount of power as a small power station.

Burning biofuels does not contribute as much as fossil fuels to global warming because the amount of carbon dioxide released is the same as was absorbed when the plants were growing.

Worked example

It has been suggested that empty North Sea oil and gas fields could be used as places to store carbon dioxide produced by power stations burning fossil fuels.

(a) Explain why carbon capture and storage (CCS) is necessary. *(2 marks)*

(b) State one reason why CCS has not been carried out yet. *(1 mark)*

(c) Why are the North Sea oil and gas field a suitable storage places? *(2 marks)*

CCS is expensive and suitable sites have not been tested yet.

(a) Carbon dioxide is produced when fossil fuels are burned. Carbon dioxide levels are rising in the atmosphere and are linked to global warming.

(b) The technology to collect and store carbon dioxide underground is still being developed.

(c) As they held oil and gas for millions of years it is thought that the carbon dioxide could be stored and wouldn't be released into the atmosphere.

Now try this

1 Tick **two** fuels that contribute to global warming when burned. *(2 marks)*

Fuel	Tick (✓)
coal	
wood	
natural gas	

2 Complete the sentence.

Using more nuclear energy instead of fossil fuels would .... global warming. *(1 mark)*

3 'Protesters oppose wind farm' is a newspaper headline. Suggest two reasons why erecting wind turbines is not popular with everyone. *(2 marks)*

Distributing electricity

In the UK, the National Grid distributes electricity from power stations to consumers.

The National Grid

Mains electricity is distributed to homes, shops, offices and factories by cables from power stations, which may be hundreds of kilometres away.

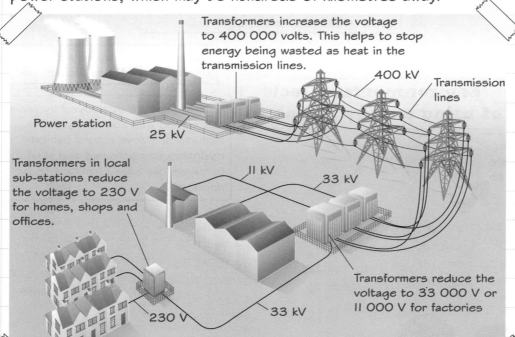

Transformers increase the voltage to 400 000 volts. This helps to stop energy being wasted as heat in the transmission lines.

400 kV

Transmission lines

Power station

25 kV

Transformers in local sub-stations reduce the voltage to 230 V for homes, shops and offices.

11 kV

33 kV

230 V

33 kV

Transformers reduce the voltage to 33 000 V or 11 000 V for factories

When electrical energy travels along a wire some of it is dissipated. Increasing the voltage to 400 kV reduces current which reduces the amount energy wasted.

High voltage is very dangerous. The electric shock caused by touching a high-voltage cable can kill.

Worked example

target D–C

SPEC AQA SKILL

Compare the advantages and disadvantages of burying high voltage cables underground with hanging them overhead from pylons. *(4 marks)*

Advantages. Burying cables is much more expensive than carrying them on pylons. It is more difficult to make repairs to buried cables than to those above ground.

Disadvantages. Pylons are a form of visual pollution. People can be injured if they climb pylons but are unlikely to be injured by buried cables.

EXAM ALERT!

Note where the step-up and step-down transformers are in the National Grid. You do not need to know how transformers are built or work but you do need to know what they do and why.

Students have struggled with this topic in recent exams – **be prepared!**

Now try this

target G–E

1 Draw a ring around the correct phrase to complete the sentence below.

The National Grid carries electricity at a

> very high voltage.
> very high current.
> very low voltage.

(1 mark)

target D–C

2 Describe how step-up and step-down transformers are used in the National Grid. *(2 marks)*

Physics six mark question 2

There will be one 6 mark question on your exam paper which will be marked for *Quality of Written Communication as well as scientific knowledge*. This means that you need to apply your scientific knowledge, present your answer in a logical and organised way and make sure that your spelling, grammar and punctuation are as good as you can make them.

Worked example

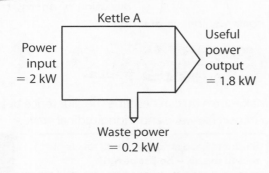
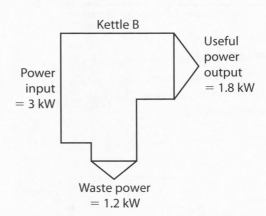

A scientist tested two kettles to see which was the most efficient. He boiled 1 litre of water in each kettle and the water took 3 minutes to boil. Use the information in the Sankey diagram to compare the efficiency of the two kettles. *(6 marks)*

The two kettles provide the same amount of useful power (1.8 kW), although kettle B uses more power (3 kW instead of 2 kW). This is because kettle A is more efficient.

This means that less of the energy provided to kettle A is wasted than for kettle B. The wasted energy is transferred as heat, which heats up the kettle and the surrounding air.

The efficiency of kettle A is 1.8 kW/2 kW = 0.9

The efficiency of kettle B is 1.8 kW/3 kW = 0.6

Although both kettles take the same length of time to boil 1 litre of water, kettle A uses less energy.

You should explain terms such as **efficiency**.

The question says to **compare** the two kettles, so you should write about both kettles, saying what is similar or different about them.

You should use data from the diagrams and from calculations to work out a full answer and be able to compare the kettles.

Now try this

Burning fossil fuels provided 69% of all the electricity generated in the UK in 2011. 2.5% of UK electricity was provided by biofuels, hydroelectric, wind and solar power, which are renewable sources of energy. Describe the impact of fossil fuels and renewable sources of energy on the environment. *(6 marks)*

Properties of waves

Waves transfer energy from one place to another. Waves are carried by something that is oscillating.

Transverse

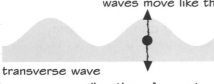

water and electromagnetic waves move like this

transverse wave

direction of wave travel

direction of energy transfer

vs

Longitudinal

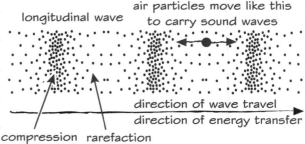

longitudinal wave   air particles move like this to carry sound waves

compression   rarefaction

direction of wave travel

direction of energy transfer

Mechanical waves must move through solids, liquids or gases. They cannot travel through a vacuum. They may be transverse or longitudinal.

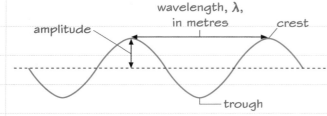

amplitude

wavelength, λ, in metres   crest

trough

Frequency, f, is the number of complete waves passing a point in 1 second, in hertz, Hz. The wave equation is, $v = f \times \lambda$, where v is the velocity in metres per second, m/s

---

Worked example   D-C

The sound of a whistle has a frequency of 680 Hz and a wavelength of 0.5 m.

(a) Calculate the speed of the sound through air.   *(2 marks)*

(b) Explain why sound is a type of mechanical wave.   *(2 marks)*

Make sure the data you have been given are in the correct units.

(a) $v = f \times \lambda = 680 \text{ Hz} \times 0.5 \text{ m}$
$= 340 \text{ m/s}$

(b) Sound is a mechanical wave because it needs a solid, liquid or gas to oscillate.

Now try this

G-E

D-C

1 A long stretched spring is fixed at one end. By pushing and pulling it, parts of the spring become compressed. The oscillations travel along the spring and hit the fixed end four times a second. The compressed parts of the spring are 0.75 metres apart.

State the type of wave that is produced in the spring.   *(1 mark)*

2 Calculate the speed of the wave along the spring in the question above.   *(2 marks)*

Electromagnetic waves

ELECTROMAGNETIC waves are transverse waves that include light, radio waves and X-rays. All of these waves travel at the same speed in a vacuum. The different types of electromagnetic wave form a continuous spectrum.

shortest wavelength, highest frequency, most energy   longest wavelength, lowest frequency, least energy

10^{-15} m 10^{-9} m 10^{-6} m 10^{-3} m   1 m 10^{4} m

gamma and X-rays — ultra-violet rays (UV) — visible light — infrared — micro-waves — radio waves

> 'Continuous' means that there are no breaks in the spectrum and one type of wave merges into the next.

(Gamma and X rays) cause cancers

(UV) causes sunburn and skin cancer

(vis) can damage eyes

(IR) heating effect may cause burning

(microwave) hazards not proven

Communications

Some electromagnetic waves are used in communication because the waves can carry information with the energy they transfer.

Hazards of electromagnetic waves:
- Gamma and X rays cause cancer.
- UV causes sunburn and skin cancer.
- Visual can damage eyes.
- Infrared can cause burning.

Worked example   target G-E

Compare the way that microwaves and infrared are used for communications. *(2 marks)*

Infrared is used for communicating over a short distance, such as a TV remote control. Microwaves are used over longer distances, such as for satellite TV.

> Make sure that you use the data you have been given in the question. This is just one study. Some other studies suggest there is a link between mobile phones and cancer.

Worked example   target G-E

SPEC AQA SKILL

Between 1992 and 2008 the percentage of people with mobile phones went from 0% to almost 100%. The number of brain tumours remained the same. A scientist concluded that there was no link between mobile phones and brain tumours. Do you agree? Explain your answer. *(2 marks)*

I agree. If mobile phones were causing brain cancer then you would expect the number of tumours to increase as the number of people using mobile phones increased.

Now try this

target G-E

1 (a) Which type of electromagnetic wave comes between infrared and ultraviolet in wavelength? *(1 mark)*

(b) Which type of electromagnetic wave is used in remote controls? *(1 mark)*

target D-C

2 Some makes of mobile phone give out lower levels of microwave radiation than others. Suggest a reason why this may be important. *(1 mark)*

Waves

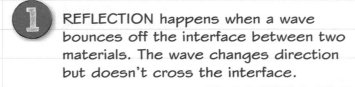

1 REFLECTION happens when a wave bounces off the interface between two materials. The wave changes direction but doesn't cross the interface.

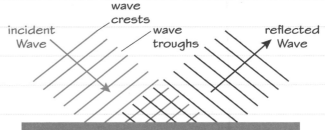

incident Wave — wave crests — wave troughs — reflected Wave

2 REFRACTION happens when a wave crosses an interface between two materials. The wave changes direction unless the rays hit the interface at right angles.

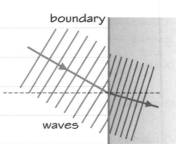

boundary

waves

3 DIFFRACTION happens when waves pass through a gap or over an obstacle that is similar in size to the wavelength of the wave. The wave spreads out through the gap.

> A ray is a line showing the direction the waves are travelling.

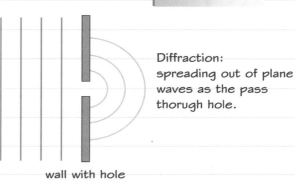

Diffraction: spreading out of plane waves as the pass thorugh hole.

wall with hole

Worked example target D-C

 AQA SPEC SKILL

Explain why it is possible to pick up radio signals in a valley but not a TV or mobile phone signal. *(3 marks)*

> Radio, TV and mobile phone signals can pass through the walls of buildings.

Radio waves have a wavelength similar to the height of hills, so they are diffracted around the hills. This means that radio waves reach places that cannot see the transmitter. Shorter wavelengths are used for TV and mobile phones, which are not diffracted by hills so there must not be any hills between your TV or mobile phone and the transmitter.

Now try this

 target E-D

1 Use the words in the box to complete the sentence.

| reflection | refraction | diffraction |

Spectacle lenses make use of .... *(1 mark)*

 target D-C

2 Compare what happens to waves when they are reflected and refracted at a boundary between two materials. *(2 marks)*

Reflection in mirrors

When waves are reflected, the angle of incidence is equal to the angle of reflection.

The INCIDENT RAY shows the direction of waves moving towards a surface.

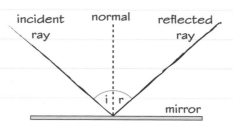

The REFLECTED RAY shows the direction after reflection.

The NORMAL is an imaginary line drawn perpendicular to the surface where the incident ray meets it.

Images in plane mirrors

When light is reflected from a PLANE mirror, an image is formed, which is VIRTUAL.

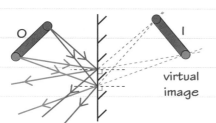

virtual image

'Plane' means flat.

'Virtual' means that the rays do not actually pass through the image. Your image in a mirror appears to be behind the mirror but the light does not come from there.

EXAM ALERT!

Make sure you can draw neat ray diagrams; you must use a ruler for these. Make sure you can draw the normal on a ray diagram.

Students have struggled with questions like this in recent exams – **be prepared!**

Worked example

A man uses a mirror to help him shave. Draw the incident and reflected rays on the diagram to show how he can see his chin. *(2 marks)*

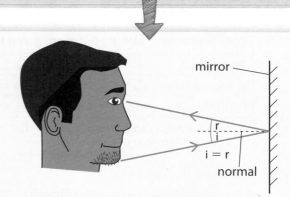

Now try this

1 (a) Choose the from the words in the boxes to complete the sentences below:

| gets larger   gets smaller   is 90°   stays the same |

If the angle that an incident ray makes with the normal gets larger, the angle the reflected ray makes with the normal .... *(1 mark)*

(b) | upright   upside down   real   virtual |

An image in a plane mirror is .... and .... *(2 marks)*

target
D-C

2 A driveway reaches the road at a right angle. A driver on the driveway uses a mirror on the opposite side of the road to see cars approaching from the left. Draw a labelled ray diagram showing how the driver can see a car coming from the left while looking straight ahead. *(3 marks)*

Sound

Sound waves are longitudinal waves that cause vibrations in materials.

The material that sound waves travel through is known as the MEDIUM. Sound waves can travel through solids, liquids and gases. The PITCH of a sound is determined by its frequency. A high-pitched sound is a wave with a high frequency. The LOUDNESS of a sound is related to the amplitude of the vibrations.

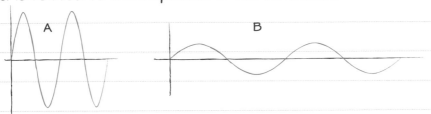

A and B are two sound waves. B has a lower pitch than A but A is louder

It is easier to show sound waves as if they are displayed on an oscilloscope. The higher the peak, the more the particles are compressed.

Echoes

Sound waves can be reflected off surfaces. We hear the reflections as ECHOES. Echoes arrive after the main sound because the waves have travelled further.

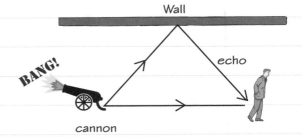

Worked example G-E

1 Some statements about sound are given below. Tick (✓) two statements that are true.

Statement	Tick (✓)
In sound waves, particles vibrate in the same direction as the wave travels	✓
Sound waves can travel through gases and a vacuum	
A sound wave with a frequency of 512 Hz has a higher pitch than one with a frequency of 256 Hz	✓

2 Complete the sentence.
A sound wave with a large amplitude is <u>louder</u> than one with a small amplitude.

EXAM ALERT!

Remember that the pitch of a sound is determined by its frequency and that the loudness of a sound is determined by its amplitude.

Students have struggled with questions like this in recent exams – **be prepared!**

Now try this

D-C

1 Explain what type of wave whales use to communicate. *(2 marks)*

2 Explain why an echo always arrives after the original sound.

(2 marks)

Red-shift

The Doppler effect can be used to measure the speed and direction of moving objects.

The Doppler Effect

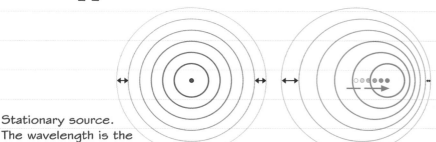

Stationary source. The wavelength is the same on both sides.

When a source of a wave is moving, the waves in front of it get squashed. Their frequency increases and wavelength decreases. The waves behind the source become stretched. Their frequency is lower and wavelength longer.

The faster the source moves the bigger the change in frequency and wavelength. If the source of a sound is coming towards us we hear a higher pitched sound. If the source is moving away the sound is at a lower pitch.

Red-shift

galaxy moving away

The radiation from stars in distant galaxies is at longer wavelengths than radiation from similar stars in our own galaxy. This is called red-shift. Red-shift shows that the galaxies are moving away from us.

The further the galaxies are from us the bigger the red-shift. This means that the further away the stars are the faster they are moving away from us.

Red-shift does not just apply to visible light, but to radio, microwave and other electromagnetic waves too.

Worked example

target D-C

An astronomer observes two galaxies. The light from galaxy A is red-shifted more than galaxy B. State **two** conclusions the astronomer can make. *(2 marks)*

Galaxy A is moving away from Earth faster than B. Galaxy A is further away than B.

Now try this

target G-E

target D-C

1 A fire engine with its siren sounding is travelling away from you. Which row in the table describes the changes to the sound of the siren? *(1 mark)*

2 Describe the observations that reveal to astronomers that distant galaxies are moving away from us faster than galaxies that are closer. *(2 marks)*

Answer	Wavelength	Pitch
A	longer	lower
B	longer	higher
C	shorter	lower
D	shorter	higher

Expanding universe

Observations of red-shift provide evidence for theories about the universe.

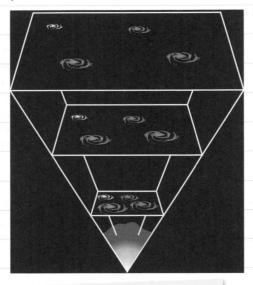

Red shift shows astronomers that the universe is expanding. The Big Bang theory suggests that the universe began from a tiny point and expanded to become what we see now.

Time

The Big Bang theory predicts that the radiation released when the universe started to expand is still present. As the universe expanded the wavelength increased so that it is now microwaves. This Cosmic Microwave Background Radiation (CMBR) has been observed and is evidence for the Big Bang theory.

The Big Bang is not like a normal explosion, which blows material into space. Since the Big Bang, space itself has expanded so that everything in the universe has moved apart.

The Big Bang is the only theory for the origin of the universe that is accepted by scientists today.

Worked example

SPEC AQA SKILL

1 Explain why the observations of red-shift of galaxies was evidence for the Big Bang theory of the universe. *(2 marks)*

2 The Big Bang theory successfully explains observations made by astronomers but has limitations, like all scientific models. State two limitations of the Big Bang theory. *(2 marks)*

1 Red-shift observations showed that all the distant galaxies were moving apart, so in the past they must have been closer together.

2 The model cannot describe what happened before the Big Bang or what happens beyond the furthest part of the universe we can see.

The Big Bang also cannot explain why the expansion of the universe is getting faster.

Now try this

target G-E

1 Choose the true statement from the following sentences about the CMBR. *(1 mark)*

A: The CMBR is given off by all the stars we can see.

B: The CMBR comes from the centre of the universe.

C: The CMBR is the glow we see when we look into the night sky.

D: The CMBR comes from the radiation present shortly after the universe began.

target D-C

2 The Big Bang theory is accepted by most scientists because it explains the observations that astronomers have made. Give **two** pieces of evidence and explain how they support the Big Bang theory. *(4 marks)*

Physics six mark question 3

There will be one 6 mark question on your exam paper which will be marked for *Quality of Written Communication as well as scientific knowledge.* This means that you need to apply your scientific knowledge, present your answer in a logical and organised way and make sure that your spelling, grammar and punctuation are as good as you can make them.

Worked example

Compare the properties and uses of microwaves and radio waves. *(6 marks)*

Microwaves and radio waves are both types of electromagnetic radiation. They are transverse waves that can travel through a vacuum at the speed of light. Radio waves have the longer wavelength and therefore have the lower frequency. Microwaves carry more energy. They can be used in microwave cookers to transfer energy to food.

Both types of radiation can be reflected by surfaces, absorbed or refracted when they pass through materials and diffracted when they pass through gaps.

Both types of radiation are used in communications. The longer wavelength of radio waves means that they can be diffracted around buildings and hills. This means that radio receivers can pick up radio communications even if they are not in line of sight with the transmitter. The shorter wavelength of microwaves means that a mobile phone must be on a straight line from a transmitter.

Writing your answer

The question uses the command COMPARE, so you should describe the similarities *and* differences in microwave and radio waves, and their uses in communications.

Write your answers in full sentences and check your spellings, particularly of technical words.

 Recall the properties that all types of electromagnetic radiation have.

 Show that you understand that the wavelength and frequency of waves are related.

 Remember that all waves can be reflected, refracted and diffracted.

Now try this

Most scientists agree that the Big Bang theory explains how the universe we see today was formed. Describe what the Big Bang theory is and the evidence that supports it.   *(6 marks)*

Periodic Table

Key

relative atomic mass
atomic symbol
name
atomic (proton)number

Example:

1
H
hydrogen
1

1	2											3	4	5	6	7	0
																	4 **He** helium 2
7 **Li** lithium 3	9 **Be** beryllium 4											11 **B** boron 5	12 **C** carbon 6	14 **N** nitrogen 7	16 **O** oxygen 8	19 **F** fluorine 9	20 **Ne** neon 10
23 **Na** sodium 11	24 **Mg** magnesium 12											27 **Al** aluminium 13	28 **Si** silicon 14	31 **P** phosphorous 15	32 **S** sulfur 16	35.5 **Cl** chlorine 17	40 **Ar** argon 18
39 **K** potassium 19	40 **Ca** calcium 20	45 **Sc** scandium 21	48 **Ti** titanium 22	51 **V** vanadium 23	52 **Cr** chromium 24	55 **Mn** manganese 25	56 **Fe** iron 26	59 **Co** cobalt 27	59 **Ni** nickel 28	64 **Cu** copper 29	65 **Zn** zinc 30	70 **Ga** callium 31	73 **Ge** germanium 32	75 **As** arsenic 33	79 **Se** selenium 34	80 **Br** bromine 35	84 **Kr** krypton 36
85 **Rb** rubidium 37	88 **Sr** strontium 38	89 **Y** yttrium 39	91 **Zr** zirconium 40	93 **Nb** niobium 41	96 **Mo** molybdenum 42	99 **Tc** technetium 43	101 **Ru** ruthenium 44	103 **Rh** rhodium 45	106 **Pd** palladium 46	108 **Ag** silver 47	112 **Cd** cadmium 48	115 **In** indium 49	119 **Sn** tin 50	122 **Sb** antimony 51	128 **Te** tellurium 52	127 **I** iodine 53	131 **Xe** xenon 54
133 **Cs** caesium 55	137 **Ba** barium 56	139 **La** lanthanum 4	178 **Hf** hafnium 72	181 **Ta** tantalum 73	184 **W** tungsten 74	186 **Re** rhenium 75	190 **Os** osmium 76	192 **Ir** iridium 77	195 **Pt** platinum 78	197 **Au** gold 79	201 **Hg** mercury 80	204 **Tl** thallium 81	207 **Pb** lead 82	209 **Bi** bismuth 83	210 **Po** polonium 84	211 **At** astatine 85	222 **Rn** radon 86
223 **Fr** francium 87	226 **Ra** radium 88	227 **Ac** actinium 89	261 **Rf** rutherfordium 104	262 **Db** dubnium 105	266 **Sg** seaborgium 106	264 **Bh** bohrium 107	277 **Hs** hassium 108	268 **Mt** meitnerium 109	271 **Ds** darmstadtium 110	272 **Rg** roentgenium 111							

The lanthanides (atomic numbers 58–71) and the actinides (atomic numbers 58–71) have been omitted.
Elements with atomic numbers 112–116 have been reported but not fully authenticated.

Chemistry data sheet

Reactivity series of metals

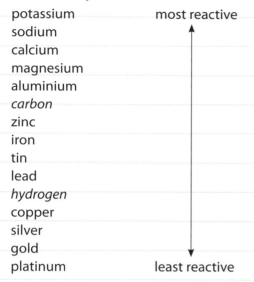

potassium   most reactive
sodium
calcium
magnesium
aluminium
carbon
zinc
iron
tin
lead
hydrogen
copper
silver
gold
platinum   least reactive

Elements in italics, though non-metals, have been included for comparison.

Formulae of some common ions

Positive ions		**Negative ions**	
Name	**Formula**	**Name**	**Formula**
hydrogen	H^+	chloride	Cl^-
sodium	Na^+	bromide	Br^-
silver	Ag^+	fluoride	F^-
potassium	K^+	iodide	I^-
lithium	Li^+	hydroxide	OH^-
ammonium	NH_4^+	nitrate	NO_3^-
barium	Ba^{2+}	oxide	O^{2-}
calcium	Ca^{2+}	sulfide	S^{2-}
copper(II)	Cu^{2+}	sulfate	SO_4^{2-}
magnesium	Mg^{2+}	carbonate	CO_3^{2-}
zinc	Zn^{2+}		
lead	Pb^{2+}		
iron(II)	Fe^{2+}		
iron(III)	Fe^{3+}		
aluminium	Al^{3+}		

Answers

You will find some advice next to some of the answers. This is written in italics. It is not part of the mark scheme but just gives you a little more information.

Biology answers

1. A healthy diet

1. Any two from: carbohydrates, fats, proteins (2).
2. Not getting the right balance of energy and nutrients (1).

2. Controlling mass

1. the rate at which all the reactions in the body are carried out (1)
2. Programme A (1); because people on this programme lost the most weight after 12 weeks (1), and also had the greatest weight loss after 1 year (1).
3. Eating less means that you take in less energy (1); exercising more increases the amount of energy you expend (1). If you can expend more energy than you take in, you will lose mass (1).

3. Lifestyle and disease

1. a lack of a nutrient in the diet (1)
2. because too much sugar in the diet can lead to Type 2 diabetes (1)
3. Exercise can help to control weight, and so reduce obesity (1), which is linked to many health problems such as Type 2 diabetes (1).

4. Pathogens and infection

1. Any one from: damaging cells when they are inside them; producing toxins/poisons (1).
2. Washing cleans pathogens off hands (1). This prevents the pathogens from one patient infecting the next patient that the doctor examines (1).
3. When we are infected, it takes a while for pathogens to reproduce inside us (1) and make a large enough number of pathogens to make us feel ill (1).

5. The immune system

1. antibodies that destroy pathogens (1), and antitoxins that destroy the toxins produced by pathogens (1)
2. (a) Your immune system remembers how to respond to the pathogen that causes measles (1) and will destroy another infection of measles so quickly that you do not fall ill (1).
   (b) The antibodies that destroy the pathogen which causes measles will not destroy the pathogen which causes chickenpox (1). So the pathogen that causes chickenpox could be able to grow fast enough to make you ill (1).

6. Immunisation

1. (a) a dead or inactive form of the pathogen that causes polio (1)
   (b) antibodies (1); immune (1)
2. (a) There is a very small risk that the child might suffer a serious illness as a result of having the vaccine (1).
   (b) There is a much greater risk of serious illness if the child has one of the diseases (1).

7. Treating diseases

1. a medicine that is used to kill bacterial pathogens inside the body (1)
2. answer 2 (1)

8. Cultures

1. High temperature kills microorganisms/sterilises equipment and media (1).
2. In industrial cultures, people don't come into contact with the bacteria (1) so they are not at risk of infection from the very large numbers of microorganisms that have grown rapidly at the higher temperatures (1).
3. Any three from: blown in from the air; transferred by touch; in the culture medium on the equipment (3)

9. Biology six mark question 1

Answers can be found on pages 99–100.

10. Receptors

1. the ear (1)
2. (a) stimulus: touching sharp pin (1); response: moving hand away (1)
   (b) pain receptors in the skin (1)

11. Responses

1. synapse (1)
2. motor neurone (1)
3. The reflex arc consists of a sensory neurone that carries the electrical impulse from the receptor to the central nervous system (1). The impulse passes to a relay neurone which carries the impulse to a motor neurone (1). The motor neurone carries the impulse to the effector (1).

12. Controlling internal conditions

1. Any two from: lungs when we breathe out; in sweat from skin; in urine from kidneys (2).
2. Any one from: in sweat from skin; in urine from kidneys (1).
3. One possible answer is: hormone FSH (1), secreted by pituitary gland (1), target organ the ovaries (1).

13. The menstrual cycle

1. (a) Any three from: follicle-stimulating hormone/FSH; luteinising hormone/LH; oestrogen; progesterone (3).
   (b) FSH in pituitary gland (1), LH in pituitary gland (1), oestrogen in ovaries (1)
2. Progesterone and oestrogen inhibit/prevent the release of FSH by the pituitary gland (1). If there is no FSH, then no egg matures in the ovary (1). So no egg is released that could result in pregnancy (1).

14. Increasing fertility

1. hormones/FSH and LH (1) that cause eggs to mature and be released (1)
2. fertilisation of eggs outside a woman's body (1)
3. The woman is given fertility drugs that contain FSH, which makes eggs mature in her ovaries (1). The drugs also contain LH, which stimulates mature eggs to be released (1). The released eggs are collected and fertilised with sperm outside her body (1). When the embryos have developed into tiny balls of cells, one or two are placed in the woman's womb to develop until birth (1).

15. Plant responses

1. the way a plant grows in response to light **(1)**
2. Auxin stimulates shoot cells to elongate **(1)**. Auxin inhibits (reduces) the elongation of root cells **(1)**.
3. Gravity causes auxin to move to the lower side of the shoot **(1)**. So cells on the lower side of the shoot are inhibited in elongation/don't elongate as much compared with cells on the upper side **(1)**. So the cells on the upper side grow longer than those on the lower side and the root curves downwards **(1)**.

16. Plant hormones

1. as weedkillers/herbicides **(1)**, in rooting powder **(1)**
2. Rooting powder contains plant hormones **(1)**. The hormones stimulate the end of the cutting to develop roots **(1)**.
3. The hormones kill the weeds in the crops **(1)** without harming the crop plants **(1)**.

17. New drugs

1. something that looks like a drug but doesn't contain any drug **(1)**
2. in the laboratory on cells, tissues or animals **(1)**; in small doses on healthy volunteers **(1)**; in larger doses on patients with the disease that the drug is supposed to work on **(1)**
3. to make sure they are safe/not toxic **(1)**; to make sure they work as expected/ test their efficacy **(1)**; to find the right dose for treatment **(1)**

18. Thalidomide and statins

1. **(a)** treating problems with sleeping **(1)**
   (b) treating leprosy **(1)**
2. medical drug **(1)**, heart/circulatory disease **(1)**
3. The drug was not tested on pregnant women **(1)**, so the effect was not seen until after women had used it **(1)**.

19. Recreational drugs

1. Legal: one from alcohol or nicotine **(1)**; illegal: one from ecstasy, cannabis, heroin, etc. **(1)**.
2. It can cause mental health problems/mental illness **(1)**.
3. They are dependent on/addicted to the drug **(1)** so they will suffer distressing withdrawal symptoms if they stop taking it **(1)**.

20. Drugs and health

1. because they can have harmful side effects **(1)**
2. **(a)** because if used sensibly, it is safe to drink **(1)**
   (b) If drunk in large quantities, it can damage the body **(1)**.

21. Drugs in sport

1. Any one from: stimulants, anabolic steroids **(1)**.
2. Any one from: can give an unfair advantage to those who use them compared with those who don't; side effects of drug harm athletes **(1)**.
3. Increased heart rate delivers more oxygen and food to muscles **(1)**, so the muscles can release more energy, making the athlete faster or stronger in their sport **(1)**.

22. Biology six mark question 2

Answers can be found on page 100.

23. Competition

1. food **(1)**, mates **(1)**, territory **(1)**
2. Any one from: using bright colour to advertise that they are poisonous; use colour to create an impression of being much bigger **(1)**.
3. so that the plants don't compete **(1)** for an environmental factor such as light/water/nutrients **(1)**

24. Adaptations

1. Any one from: thick fur or fat below skin, white fur, small ears, wide feet **(1)**.
2. extreme heat **(1)**
3. Appropriate answer for Q1 response, e.g.: thick fur and fat below skin – to insulate against heat loss from body to air; white fur – camouflage against white snow; small ears – reduce heat loss to air; wide feet – to provide grip on slippery ice/stop bear sinking into snow **(1)**.

25. Indicators

1. how widely spread an organism is in the environment **(1)**
2. Some species of invertebrates are only found in unpolluted water and others only in highly polluted water **(1)**. So by looking at what species are in the water you can see how polluted it is **(1)**.
3. oxygen level **(1)**, which is high in unpolluted water and low in polluted water **(1)**

26. Energy and biomass

1. photosynthesis **(1)**
2. Some of the energy in the biomass will be lost to the environment in the rabbit's waste materials/faeces **(1)**. Some of the biomass will be broken down in respiration **(1)**.

27. Decay

1. The breakdown/digestion of dead or waste materials **(1)**; this breakdown is caused by microorganisms **(1)**.
2. Warmth from the Sun will increase the rate of growth of microorganisms in the heap so they break the materials in the heap down faster **(1)**.
3. Each crop that is grown in the ground takes nutrients out of the soil leaving fewer nutrients for the next crop **(1)**. Fewer nutrients means the plants won't grow as much, so they will produce a smaller yield **(1)**.

28. Carbon cycling

1. Any one from: combustion, respiration **(1)**.
2. Any one from: carbohydrates, fats, proteins **(1)**.
3. Microorganisms and detritus feeders break down the waste **(1)**. The microorganisms and detritus use some of the materials from the waste for respiration which releases carbon dioxide into the air **(1)**.

29. Genes

1. nucleus **(1)**
2. genes **(1)**, environment/conditions during development **(1)**

30. Reproduction

1. **(a)** one **(1)**   **(b)** two **(1)**
2. sexual reproduction **(1)**
3. They all have the same one parent/there has been no mixing of genes **(1)**. So they are genetically identical **(1)**.

31. Cloning

1. Any one from: embryo transplant, adult cell cloning **(1)**.
2. **(a)** Any one suitable answer such as: use pieces of an adult plant, produces clones of the adult plant **(1)**. *Just saying they are both done with plants is not enough because that information is given in the question.*
   (b) Any one suitable answer such as: plant tissue culture uses only a few plant cells, but cuttings use much larger pieces of stem, root or leaf **(1)**.

3. One adult animal provides a body cell, from which the nucleus is removed and used in the process **(1)**. An adult female provides the unfertilised egg cell from which the nucleus is removed and thrown away, and the rest of the cell used in the process **(1)**. The developing embryo is then placed into the womb of another female to grow and develop **(1)**.

32. Genetic engineering

1. cutting a gene out of a chromosome of one organism **(1)** and putting it into a chromosome inside a cell of a different organism **(1)**
2. The gene for herbicide resistance is put into some plant cells **(1)**. The cells are treated/grown by tissue culture so they develop into new plants **(2)**.

33. Issues with new science

1. Any one from: A decrease in the number of insects will affect the animals that eat them; the insects will develop resistance to the chemical in the plants and not be affected by it **(1)**.
2. If the weeds become herbicide-resistant, the farmer won't be able to kill them with herbicide and so the weeds will compete with the crop and reduce crop yield **(1)**. This means the farmer will get less money when the crop is sold **(1)**.

34. Evolution

1. Organisms are classified into different groups, such as animals, plants and microorganisms **(1)**, by how similar or different their characteristics are **(1)**.
2. **(a)** It shows that cows and pigs are more similar to each other **(1)** than they are to humans **(1)**.
   (b) cow and pig **(1)** because the tree shows that the common ancestor of the cow and hedgehog lived further back in time than the common ancestor of the cow and pig **(1)**

35. Theories of evolution

1. **(a)** Jack developed his ability to swim by training **(1)**. His daughter inherited his champion ability **(1)**.
   (b) Jack inherited characteristics from his parents that made it possible for him to become a champion swimmer by training **(1)**. His daughter inherited these characteristics from Jack and so could also become a champion swimmer by training **(1)**.
   (c) We now know about genes **(1)** and can explain how characteristics are passed from parent to child **(1)**.

36. Biology six mark question 3

Answers can be found on page 100.

Chemistry answers

37. Atoms and elements

1. **(a)** nucleus **(1)**
   (b) electrons **(1)**
2. **(a)** Sodium is made of only one sort of atom/it is made from sodium atoms only **(1)**.
   (b) Oxygen is a non-metal/oxygen is in a different group/oxygen is a different element **(1)**.

38. Particles in atoms

1. 4 **(1)**
2. **(a)** (i) ○ **(1)**   (ii) ● **(1)**   (iii) ✕ **(1)**
   (b) 8 **(1)**

39. Electronic structure

1. **(a)** 2,4 **(1)**
   (b) 2,8,6 **(1)**
   (c) 2,8,8,2 **(1)**
2.

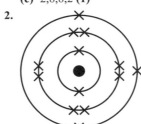

1 mark for 13 crosses drawn; **1** mark for correct number of crosses in each circle (2,8,3)

40. Electronic structure and groups

1. 1 **(1)**
2. Their atoms all have one electron in their highest energy level **(1)**.
3. 8 **(1)**; except for helium, which has 2

41. Making compounds

1. Boxes 3 and 4 ticked for one mark each **(2)**
2. Covalent **(1)**

42. Chemical equations

1. 50 g – 22 g = 28 g **(1)**
2. **(a)** Lead nitrate and potassium iodide are reactants/react together **(1)**; lead iodide and potassium nitrate are products/made in the reaction **(1)**.
   (b) stays the same **(1)**
3. No atoms are made or lost in chemical reactions **(1)**, and there are two H atoms and two F atoms on each side **(1)**.

43. Limestone

1. Any two from the following for one mark each: new jobs, makes money, provides building materials, makes useful products (or named product such as cement) **(2)**.
2. Limestone: Two from the following for one mark each: relatively easy to cut, attractive appearance, natural material (no processing needed) **(2)**. OR

   Concrete: Two from the following for one mark each: resistant to weathering (for example, from acid rain), stronger than limestone, can be reinforced with steel, can be moulded on site into different shapes **(2)**.

44. Calcium carbonate chemistry

1. copper oxide **(1)**
2. **(a)** Carbon dioxide turns limewater cloudy **(1)**.
   (b) calcium carbonate **(1)**
3. calcium oxide + water → calcium hydroxide **(1)**
4. Sodium carbonate reacts with acids to produce carbon dioxide **(1)**, which escapes as bubbles of gas **(1)**.

45. Chemistry six mark question 1

Answers can be found on page 100.

46. Extracting metals

1. copper oxide + carbon → copper + carbon dioxide (correct reactants, **1**; correct products, **1**)

2. **(a)** An ore is a rock containing a metal/metal compound **(1)** with enough metal to make it economical to extract the metal **(1)**.

   (b) reduction **(1)**

3. Electrolysis of a molten potassium compound **(1)** because potassium is more reactive than carbon **(1)**.

47. Extracting copper

1. Boxes 1 and 4 ticked for one mark each **(2)**

2. Supplies of high-grade copper ores are running out/only low-grade copper ores left in the future **(1)**; copper is extracted from copper ore so future supplies may be limited **(1)**.

48. Recycling metals

1. Advantage: less carbon dioxide is produced **(1)**. Disadvantage: used steel items must be collected and transported **(1)**.

2. Two from the following for one mark each: less waste rock produced; less carbon dioxide (or named pollutant) produced; less waste sent to landfill **(2)**.

49. Steel and other alloys

1. resistant to corrosion **(1)**

2. A mixture of metals/a mixture of a metal and another element **(1)**

3. Iron from the blast furnace contains impurities **(1)**, which make it brittle **(1)**.

50. Transition metals

1. Named transition metal other than copper or iron, e.g. titanium (not aluminium) **(1)**

2. **(a)** Aluminium is not as strong as steel **(1)**.

   (b) Aluminium is less dense than steel/aluminium does not corrode **(1)**.

3. Titanium **(1)**; because although both metals are resistant to corrosion **(1)** titanium has a low density/is lighter for its size **(1)**.

51. Hydrocarbons and alkanes

1. C_8H_{18} **(1)**

2. **(a)** contains only single bonds (between carbon atoms) **(1)**

   (b) compound of hydrogen and carbon atoms only **(1)**

3. The general formula for alkanes is C_nH_{2n+2} **(1)**, and the formula for X follows this (the number of hydrogen atoms is two plus twice the number of carbon atoms) **(1)**.

52. Crude oil and alkanes

1. Two from the following for one mark each: boiling point, viscosity, flammability **(2)**.

2. They have different boiling points (or different ranges of boiling points) **(1)**.

3. Oil is vaporised **(1)** passed into column which is hot at bottom and cool at top **(1)** alkanes rise and condense at different heights/levels **(1)**.

53. Combustion

1. oxygen/O_2 **(1)**

2. acid rain **(1)**

3. **(a)** Fuel A, because hydrocarbons contain hydrogen and carbon **(1)** and these oxidise to water vapour and carbon dioxide **(1)**.

   (b) Fuel B, because during incomplete combustion carbon oxidises **(1)** to form carbon monoxide **(1)**.

54. Biofuels

1. Carbon dioxide and water vapour are produced from ethanol **(1)**, but only water vapour from hydrogen **(1)**.

2. Less food grown/food prices increase **(1)**

55. Chemistry six mark question 2

Answers can be found on page 100.

56. Cracking and alkenes

1. **(a)** So that vapour is produced that passes over the catalyst **(1)**

   (b) Add bromine water and shake **(1)**; this turns from orange to colourless if alkenes are present **(1)**. *Writing 'clear' would not get the mark, as 'clear' just means see-through – it does not mean the same as 'colourless'.*

   (c) **(1)**

57. Making polymers

1. **(a)** ethene **(1)**

   (b) polymerisation **(1)**

2. Any two from the following: absorbs a lot of water, non-toxic (not poisonous), soft, cheap (because the nappy is disposable) **(2)**.

3. **(a)** **(1)**
   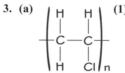

   (b) poly(chloroethene) **(1)** *not poly(chloroethane)*

58. Polymer problems

1. Cannot be broken down or decomposed by microbes **(1)**

2. The bags are biodegradable/break down easily after use **(1)**.

3. Statement for first mark with reason for second mark. For example: polymers are made from crude oil **(1)**, which is a limited resource, so recycling conserves oil **(1)**; OR recycling reduces the amount of polymer going to landfill **(1)** and we are running out of sites for landfill sites **(1)**.

59. Ethanol

1. **(a)** sugar **(1)** → carbon dioxide **(1)** + ethanol **(1)**

   (b) steam **(1)**

2. Box 2 **(1)** and box 3 **(1)**

3. Fermentation uses sugar from plants/a renewable resource **(1)**. If hydration of ethene was used, the raw material would be crude oil/a non-renewable resource **(1)**.

60. Vegetable oils

1. Boxes 2 and 4 ticked **(2)**

2. Rapeseed oil floats on water (and does not dissolve in it) **(1)**.

3. by pressing **(1)**; by distillation **(1)**

61. Emulsions

1. box 3 ticked **(1)**

2. **(a)** unsaturated oil **(1)**

   (b) Bromine water changes from orange **(1)** to colourless **(1)**.

3. An emulsifier stabilises an emulsion **(1)**; stops the ingredients separating out **(1)**. *'Clear' is not the same as 'colourless' and is not correct.*

62. The Earth's structure

1. A – mantle (1); B – core (1)
2. (a) a few centimetres per year (1)
   (b) earthquakes (1); volcanoes (1)
3. Convection currents in the mantle (1) driven by heat released by radioactive processes (1) move the plates.
4. Any one from the following: scientists cannot accurately predict when a volcano will erupt, scientists cannot predict how big an eruption will be, it is inconvenient or expensive to leave the area (1).

63. Continental drift

1. Any two from the following for one mark each: the east coast of South America fits the west coast of Africa, similar fossils are found in both continents, similar rock layers are found in both continents (2).
2. The continents were once all joined together (1), then moved apart (1).

64. The Earth's atmosphere

1. A – nitrogen (1) B – oxygen (1)
2. They released water vapour (1) which cooled and condensed (1)
3. (a) copper + oxygen → copper oxide (1)
   (b) volume of oxygen = 100 − 79 = 21 cm^3 (1); percentage of oxygen = 21/100 × 100 = 21% (1)

65. The early atmosphere

1. (a) The process that plants and algae use to make their own food (1)
   (b) oxygen (1)
2. Any two from the following for one mark each: Earth has more nitrogen, oxygen, argon; Earth has less carbon dioxide (2).
3. The percentage of oxygen has increased (1) because plants and algae have produced oxygen (1) by photosynthesis (1).

66. The early atmosphere and carbon dioxide

1. photosynthesis (1); dissolving in oceans (1); formation of fossil fuels (coal or oil) (1); formation of carbonates (limestone) (1)

67. Carbon dioxide today

1. water vapour (1); carbon dioxide (1)
2. One from the following: global warming; oceans become more acidic (1).
3. (a) They absorb large amounts of carbon dioxide from the atmosphere (1).
   (b) increased use of fossil fuels (or a specific example of this, such as more cars) (1)
   (c) One from the following: seawater becoming more acidic (pH reduced), shells of sea creatures (or coral) damaged (1).

68. Chemistry six mark question 3

Answers can be found on page 100–101.

Physics answers

69. Infrared radiation

1. B (1)
2. black (1) because it is the best absorber of radiation (1)

70. Kinetic theory

1. (a) solid (1)
   (b) shake the box (1) so that the balls move around but still touch each other (1)
   (c) shake the box more violently (1)

71. Methods of transferring energy

1. Three from: make it from an insulating material; wrap it in an insulating material; paint the surface of the mug silver/white; cover the mug with a lid (3).
2. Energy transfers from your hand into the perfume (1). As the temperature of the perfume rises more of it evaporates (1). The evaporation takes energy away from the hand and it feels cooler (1).

72. Rate of energy transfer

1. Metal is a good conductor (1). The larger the surface area the more energy is transferred from the engine to the air (1).
2. On warm days more of the water particles become a gas (1). Wind blows them away from the clothes so they cannot condense onto it again (1).

73. Keeping warm

1. (a) The filled cavity cuts the energy transferred across the cavity by convection (1), so the wall becomes a better insulator (1).
   (b) payback time = £270/£90 per year (1) = 3 years (1)

74. Specific heat capacity

1. (a) It requires the least amount of energy to raise the temperature of the copper and the most for the aluminium because of the size of the their specific heat capacities (1), so the time taken to supply the energy to the copper by the hotplate is least (1).
   (b) energy = 1.2 kg × 460 J/kg°C × 80°C (1) = 44 160 J (1) (or 44.16 kJ)

75. Energy and efficiency

1. (a) Sankey diagram with widths of arrows correctly drawn to scale (1), labelled showing electrical energy used 80 J, energy wasted 60 J and useful energy (light) 20 J (1). *The exact positioning of the arrows might be slightly different.*
   (b) light/sound (1)

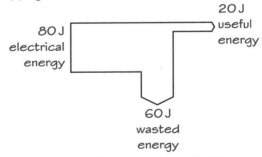

2. Efficiency = 20 J/ 80 J (1) = 0.25 or 25% (1)
3. It will use less power/energy to do the same job or less power/energy wasted (1), so the costs will be lower or will pay back the cost of the new washing machine (1).

76. Physics six mark question 1

Answers can be found on page 101.

77. Electrical appliances

1. first and third box ticked (1)
2. (a) E = 3 W × 4 × 60 s (1) = 720 J (1)
   (b) E = 0.04 kW × 2 h (1) = 0.08 kWh (1) cost = 0.08 kWh × 12p = 0.96p (1)

78. Choosing appliances

1. A: 60 min, B: 100 min **(1)**
2. **(a)** B takes in energy from the surroundings **(1)** at a lower rate/more slowly **(1)** than A.
   (b) improve the insulation **(1)**

79. Generating electricity

1. B **(1)**
2. coal burned to heat water in a boiler to make steam **(1)**; steam turns a turbine **(1)**; turbine drives a generator **(1)**
3. Nuclear power stations are expensive to build **(1)** and to decommission/take down **(1)**. *You could also say that nuclear power stations require expensive safety measures.*

80. Renewables

1. **(a)** Any two from: the solar cells don't work at night; they produce less in winter when the days are shorter; they produce less when it is cloudy; the family may need to consume more power in winter (for example, for heating) **(2)**
   (b) They could store electrical energy when it is not needed **(1)**; in batteries/pumped storage/other storage method **(1)**; they could generate electrical energy using wind turbine/small-scale hydroelectric/burning wood/biofuel **(1)**.

81. Environment and energy

1. coal **(1)** and natural gas **(1)**
2. decrease **(1)**
3. Protesters say that wind turbines are visual pollutants **(1)** and produce noise pollution **(1)**. *Stating that the wind turbines destroy habitats where they are built and may kill birds are also acceptable answers.*

82. Distributing electricity

1. very high voltage **(1)**
2. Step-up transformers increase the voltage from power stations delivered to the cables **(1)**; step-down transformers reduce the voltage supplied to homes/consumers **(1)**.

83. Physics six mark question 2

Answers can be found on page 101.

84. Properties of waves

1. longitudinal **(1)**
2. $v = 4\ \text{Hz} \times 0.75\ \text{m}$ **(1)** $= 3\ \text{m/s}$ **(1)**

85. Electromagnetic waves

1. **(a)** visible **(1)**   **(b)** infrared **(1)**
2. The lower level may be safer to use **(1)**.

86. Waves

1. refraction **(1)**
2. Reflected waves do not cross the boundary but refracted waves do **(1)**; reflected waves and refracted waves change direction **(1)**.

87. Reflection in mirrors

1. **(a)** gets larger **(1)**
   (b) upright **(1)**; virtual **(1)** *either order*
2. A diagram with a mirror opposite the driveway at an angle of about 45° **(1)**; rays from a car on the road reflected off the mirror to the driver in the driveway **(1)**; with the angle of incidence equal to the angle of reflection **(1)**

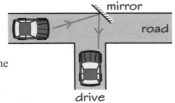

88. Sound

1. Whales use sound waves **(1)**, because they travel through water **(1)**.
2. The echo always takes a longer path than the original sound **(1)**, and this takes more time **(1)**.

89. Red-shift

1. A **(1)**
2. Light from the more distant galaxies is red-shifted **(1)** more than **(1)** light from the galaxies that are closer.

90. Expanding universe

1. D **(1)**
2. Observations of red-shift **(1)** show that galaxies are moving apart **(1)**. The cosmic microwave background radiation/CMBR **(1)** fills the universe/comes from every direction in space **(1)**. *Background radiation or microwaves will be accepted instead of CMBR.*

91. Physics six mark question 3

Answers can be found on page 101.

Six mark question answers

Each 6 mark question has a specific set of answers but here are some general comments about the answers to these questions:

NTT answer guidance:

- A basic answer is usually badly organized, has only basic information in it, does not use scientific words and includes poor spelling, punctuation and grammar.

- A good answer usually contains accurate information and shows a clear understanding of the subject. The answer will have some structure and the candidate will have tried to use some scientific words, but it might not always be accurate and there may not be all the detail needed to answer the question. There will be a few errors with spelling, punctuation and grammar.

- An excellent answer contains accurate information, is detailed and is supported by relevant examples. The answer will be well organized and will contain lots of relevant scientific words that are used in the correct way. The spelling, punctuation and grammar will be almost faultless.

9. Biology six mark question 1

A basic answer: A brief explanation is given that covers either how a balanced diet or regular exercise helps you to stay healthy.

A good answer: A brief explanation is given about the ways in which a balanced diet and regular exercise help you to stay healthy or a more detailed explanation is given on about the ways in which a balanced diet or regular exercise helps you to stay healthy.

An excellent answer: A clear, balanced and detailed explanation is provided on the ways that both a balanced diet and regular exercise help you to stay healthy.

Examples of points made in the response:

- A balanced diet provides all the nutrients you need in the right proportions and so avoids malnutrition.

- These nutrients include carbohydrates, fats, proteins, also small amounts of vitamins and minerals.

- Malnutrition can lead to health problems such as deficiency diseases and Type 2 diabetes.

- The right amount of energy in the diet that balances energy expended will stop you becoming overweight or underweight.

- People who exercise regularly are more likely to stay healthy than people who don't exercise much – for example, it can help to prevent being overweight, which can increase the risk of Type 2 diabetes (other examples of ways in which exercise can affect health could be given as long as there is a clear link to how it improves health).

22. Biology six mark question 2

A basic answer: A brief description of either how hormones are used as contraceptives or how they are used in fertility treatments.

A good answer: Either a brief description of how hormones are used as contraceptives and how they are used in fertility treatments, or a more detailed explanation of how hormones are used in contraceptives or how they are used in fertility treatments.

An excellent answer: A clear, balanced, well-ordered and detailed description of how hormones are used as contraceptives and how they are used in fertility treatment.

Examples of points made in the response:

- Contraceptives contain hormones that stop FSH production.
- This means that no eggs mature.
- No eggs are released from an ovary so pregnancy is not possible/fertility is reduced.
- Oral contraceptives may contain oestrogen and progesterone.
- In fertility treatment, FSH and LH are given to a woman.
- This stimulates eggs to mature and be released from the ovaries.
- The treatment is as part of IVF to help women who do not produce high enough levels of FSH naturally/so that the chance of fertility is increased.

36. Biology six mark question 3

A basic answer: A brief description is given about the carbon cycle either involving respiration or photosynthesis, but the organisms may not be named.

A good answer: A clear description is given that involves both photosynthesis and respiration with some attempt made to name the types of organisms involved.

An excellent answer: A clear, balanced and detailed description is given, including the role of photosynthesis and respiration. Relevant organisms are named. There is some attempt made to explain the roles of microorganisms though this is likely to be at a simple level.

Examples of points made in the response:

- Respiration of all organisms (plants, algae, animals, microorganisms and detritus feeders) breaks down carbon compounds and releases carbon dioxide into the atmosphere.
- Photosynthesis by green plants and algae takes carbon dioxide from the atmosphere.
- Inside plants and algae the products of photosynthesis are converted to carbohydrates, proteins and fats.
- When organisms die, some animals and microorganisms feed on their bodies.
- When animals, microorganisms and detritus feeders digest and absorb their food, some of the carbon compounds are used to make more carbohydrates, proteins and fats in their bodies.

45. Chemistry six mark question 1

A basic answer: A brief description of either an advantage or a disadvantage of using limestone as a building material. Little information from the table is used.

A good answer: A clear description of both an advantage and a disadvantage of using limestone as a building material. Information from the table is used in support.

An excellent answer: A clear, balanced and detailed description of advantages and disadvantages of limestone as a building material, fully supported using relevant knowledge and information from the table.

Examples of points made in the response

Advantages:

- Less energy is needed to extract limestone than brick.
- Less air pollution is released (or named pollutant such as carbon dioxide).
- Reduced effect on the environment from air pollution (such as global warming).
- Natural appearance.
- Easily cut to different shapes.

Disadvantages:

- Limestone is more expensive than brick.
- Limestone has less resistance to air pollution.
- Limestone has to be quarried.
- Example of problems caused by quarries (such as noise, dust, extra traffic, destruction of habitats).

55. Chemistry six mark question 2

A basic answer: A simple description including one statement about the extraction of aluminium or copper.

A good answer: A clear description that includes either two statements about extracting aluminium or copper, or one statement about the extraction of copper and aluminium.

An excellent answer: A clear, balanced and detailed description of the ways that both aluminium and copper are extracted from their ores.

Examples of points made in the response

Aluminium extraction:

- Aluminium cannot be extracted from aluminium oxide using carbon.
- Aluminium must be extracted using electricity (electrolysis).
- Electricity is expensive.

Copper extraction:

- Copper is extracted from its ore by heating in a furnace.
- The copper is purified by electrolysis.
- Copper can also be extracted from solutions of copper salts by displacement using scrap iron.
- Copper can be extracted by phytomining.
- Copper can be extracted by bioleaching.

68. Chemistry six mark question 3

A basic answer: A brief description is given of how the plates move or at least one result of their movement is given.

A good answer: A clear description is given of the effects of the movements of tectonic plates or a clear explanation is given of how they move, or a brief explanation is given of the effects and a brief description is given of how the plates move.

An excellent answer: A clear, detailed and balanced description is given of how tectonic plates move and an explanation is also given of how they move.

Examples of points made in the response

How tectonic plates move:

- Convection currents in the mantle move the plates.
- The mantle is mostly solid but can move.
- Currents are driven by heat from natural radioactive processes.
- Plates move a few centimetres per year.

The effects of tectonic plates moving:

- Plates move apart or together.
- Mountain-building happens when plates move together.
- Plates also move against each other.
- Sudden movements cause earthquakes.
- Earthquakes can be disastrous.
- Volcanoes can also result from the movement of plates.

76. Physics six mark question 1

A basic answer: A brief description of an advantage or a disadvantage of installing double-glazing.

A good answer: Either a brief description of an advantage and a disadvantage of installing double glazing or a more detailed description of an advantage or a disadvantage of installing double glazing, including information about cost or payback time.

An excellent answer: A clear, balanced and detailed description of both the advantages and disadvantages of installing double glazing with supporting evidence from the information provided.

Examples of points made in the response:

Advantages:

- Double glazing (2.0) has a much lower U-value than single glazing (5.0).
- This means that the rate of heat transfer through a double glazed window is much lower.
- Less energy is lost from the house so the cost of energy is reduced (by £250 per year).
- Cost of replacing windows with double glazing is recovered in 20 years.

Disadvantages:

- Replacing windows with double glazing is expensive (£5000 instead of £2000).
- The payback time is the cost/savings per year (£5000/£250 per year).
- The payback time is long (20 years).
- Even double glazed windows have a high rate of heat transfer – almost as much as a cavity brick wall (1.8).

83. Physics six mark question 2

A basic answer: A brief statement about the impact of either fossil fuels or renewable sources of energy on the environment.

A good answer: A brief statement about the effects of fossil fuels and renewable sources of energy on the environment or a more detailed statement about the effect of fossil fuels or renewable sources of energy on the environment.

An excellent answer: A clear, balanced and detailed description of the impact that both fossil fuels and renewable sources of energy have on the environment with some examples of renewable sources of energy given.

Examples of points made in the response:

Fossil fuels:

- Fossil fuels release carbon dioxide into the atmosphere, which is linked to global warming.
- Fossil fuels also release acidic gases, which can cause acid rain.
- Fossil fuels produce waste materials such as ash.
- Fossil fuel power stations can produce visual pollution.
- Fossil fuels have to be extracted from the Earth and this can cause disruption of wildlife habitats (for example, oil spills).

Renewable sources of energy:

- Renewable sources of energy produce less carbon dioxide.
- Renewable sources of energy produce fewer waste materials.
- Renewable sources of energy can cause visual and noise pollution (for example, wind turbines may be very obvious in a landscape.)
- Renewable sources of energy can cause destruction of wildlife habitats (for example, flooding of valleys to build hydroelectric power stations.)
- Wind turbines can kill birds.
- Solar power farms cover a lot of land and destroy natural habitats.
- Growing biofuels takes up a lot of land and destroys natural habitats.
- Burning biofuels produces pollutants/waste materials.

91. Physics six mark question 3

A basic answer: A brief description of the Big Bang theory or a piece of evidence for the theory.

A good answer: Either a brief description of the Big Bang theory and a brief discussion of how either red-shift or the CMBR provide evidence for it, or a more detailed description of Big Bang theory or the evidence for it.

An excellent answer: A clear, balanced and detailed account of the Big bang theory and of both red-shift and the CMBR.

Examples of points made in the response.

- The Big Bang suggests that the universe expanded from a point with a burst of energy.
- The theory predicts that the universe has continued to expand.
- Observations of distant galaxies show that they are moving apart.
- And more distant galaxies are moving away faster than closer ones.
- This shows the universe is expanding.
- The evidence is from measurements of the red-shift of light received from the galaxies.
- When light is emitted from an object moving away the wavelength increases.
- The red-shift increases the further a galaxy is from us.
- The Big Bang theory predicts that energy released when the universe began is still present today.
- This background radiation fills space/cosmos.
- It is called cosmic microwave background radiation.
- The CMBR has been detected and investigated and agrees with the predictions of the Big Bang theory.
- Only the Big Bang theory explains the red-shift of the galaxies and the CMBR.

This page has been left deliberately blank.

This page has been left deliberately blank.

This page has been left deliberately blank.

This page has been left deliberately blank.

This page has been left deliberately blank.

This page has been left deliberately blank.

Revision is more than just this Guide!

You'll need plenty of practice on each topic you revise

1-to-1 page match with this Revision Guide.

Guided questions help build your confidence.

Exam-style questions on this topic.

Grades, marks and hints get you well prepared for this topic in your exam.

Had a go ☐   Nearly there ☐   Nailed it! ☐   **BIOLOGY**

A healthy diet

G-E 1   The food we eat contains a variety of nutrients.

(a) Which of these nutrients is used by the body to release energy? Tick (✓) one box.

☐ fat   ☐ minerals   ☐ vitamin   *(1 mark)*

(b) Which of these nutrients is used for the healthy functioning of the body? Tick (✓) one box.

☐ carbohydrate   ☐ protein   ☐ vitamins   *(1 mark)*

G-E 2   The table shows the nutrients present in some different foods that we eat.

Food	Nutrients present
chicken	protein and fat
rice	carbohydrate
vegetables	carbohydrate and minerals

(a) Which of the following meals gives the best nutrition? Tick (✓) one box.

☐ chicken and rice   ☐ vegetables alone   ☐ chicken and vegetables

(1 mark)

Guided   (b) Give a reason for your answer.

This meal gives a diet that is ....

This means it contains ....   *(2 marks)*

D-C 3   A healthy diet needs to contain the correct proportions of nutrients. If our diet is not balanced, we may gain or lose weight, or be malnourished.

(a) Name the two nutrients that we need the most of in a healthy diet.

> You need to look at the two largest sections of the pie chart to answer this question.

fat/sugar 7%
meat etc 12%
fruit and veg 33%
milk/dairy 15%
bread etc 33%

....   *(2 marks)*

(b) Describe what is meant by the term **malnourished**.

....   *(1 mark)*

(c) Explain how a person's diet can cause them to lose weight.

....

....   *(2 marks)*

1

Check out the matching Workbook!

THE REVISE SERIES FROM PEARSON

www.pearsonschools.co.uk/reviseaqa

Revision is more than just this Guide!

PRACTICE PAPER

Science A Chemistry
C1 practice paper

Time allowed: 60 minutes

This Practice Exam Paper has been written to help you practice what you have learned and may not be representative of a real exam paper.

1 The table shows some information about the main elements that make up the human body.

Element in body	Atomic number	Percentage (%) by mass
oxygen	8	65
carbon	6	18
hydrogen	1	10
nitrogen	7	3
calcium	20	1.5

(a) (i) What percentage (%) of the body is made of the three most abundant elements?

.... (1 mark)

(ii) Which **one** of these elements in the table is a metal? .... (1 mark)

(b) Complete the information about oxygen and hydrogen atoms in the table below.

Symbol	Atomic number	Mass number	Number of		
			protons	neutrons	electrons
O	8	16		8	8
H	1		1	0	1

(2 marks)

(c) Most of the oxygen in the body is found combined with hydrogen in water.

(i) What is the chemical formula for water? .... (1 mark)

(ii) Write a word equation for the reaction between hydrogen and oxygen that forms water and no other product.

.... (1 mark)

(d) The element calcium is mainly found in bones and teeth in the body. In nature calcium is commonly found in carbonate rocks like limestone and chalk.

The periodic table on page 131 may help you answer this question.

Draw a ring around the correct answer to complete the sentences.

The element calcium has chemical properties that are most similar to

| aluminium |
| magnesium |
| potassium |

The number of electrons in the highest energy level (outer shell) of calcium is

| 2 |
| 8 |
| 20 |

Check out the matching Workbook!

THE REVISE SERIES FROM PEARSON

www.pearsonschools.co.uk/reviseaqa

Published by Pearson Education Limited, Edinburgh Gate, Harlow, Essex, CM20 2JE.

www.pearsonschoolsandfecolleges.co.uk

Copies of official specifications for all AQA qualifications may be found on the AQA website: www.aqa.org.uk

Text and original illustrations © Pearson Education Limited 2012
Edited by Judith Head and Florence Production Ltd
Typeset and illustrated by Tech-Set Ltd, Gateshead
Cover illustration by Miriam Sturdee

The rights of Peter Ellis, Sue Kearsey and Nigel Saunders to be identified as authors of this work have been asserted by them in accordance with the Copyright, Designs and Patents Act 1988.

First published 2013

16 15 14 13 12
10 9 8 7 6 5 4 3 2 1

British Library Cataloguing in Publication Data
A catalogue record for this book is available from the British Library

ISBN 978 1 447 94210 8

Printed in Slovakia by Neografia

All other images © Pearson Education

Every effort has been made to contact copyright holders of material reproduced in this book. Any omissions will be rectified in subsequent printings if notice is given to the publishers.

In the writing of this book, no AQA examiners authored sections relevant to examination papers for which they have responsibility